Coffee with Plato

David Rossin

Solonos Press

Solonos Press,
21 Kelsall Street,
Sale,
Manchester,
M33 7TF

coffeewithplato.co.uk

Cover design by Tristam Rossin at Vector Art Gallery:
info@vectorart.gallery

ISBN 978-1-9998149-1-5

For Sally, with my love

We must do good to strangers and friends - Phaedrus

I have felt compelled to write down my thoughts about the man who came into my life whilst I was studying for my doctorate. Even as I write this, seven years later, I am still not sure who he was or whether he was telling me the truth about where he came from and his reasons for wanting to help me. There is little doubt he was a great thinker able to show the relevancy of ancient philosophy within a modern-day setting. Above all, he was a kind and generous man who came into my life at a time when I needed both academic direction and emotional support.

Without him, I would never have started this academy. He encouraged me to do something extraordinary for the good of others ... hopefully, I have.

I will never forget him.

Alecta Floros

The Health and Wellbeing Academy
Marathon
Greece

Prolegomenon

Looking back now, Plato has been present in my life from an early age. In the family home, especially in the kitchen as we ate our evening meal, his name would be mentioned with the reverence of some ancient god. I remember when I was four running my finger across the brown books of his dialogues in my Grandfather's study and watching the dust float down.

At school and at church we were taught about the miracles of Jesus but, to me as a child, Plato was just as important if not more so. He seemed to live in our neighbourhood - we didn't have to go to Galilee to find him. There were times when I thought I would meet him along the dusty track through the olive grove as I made my way back from school. At such times, I always had in mind that painting by Raphael - the one of the School of Athens with Plato and Aristotle walking towards you. In my imagination, I felt I could make them see me and stop them talking about higher things; they would bend down, smile, and give me a gift of great importance. Occasionally, on a school trip or with my family, I would go to Athens to see the Acropolis and other ancient places and, in my mind's eye, the crumpled remains were replaced by beautiful, white-stoned buildings that Plato would have known, and his feet would have trodden the very same stoned paths that still intersect the inner city.

As you can see, I had a great imagination which ripened early. I was never the day-dreamy type but, later on, I would use my fertile mind to imagine I would become an important person, not through avarice, but by passing on some special gift to mankind. Perhaps I have achieved that after all – it is not for me to judge.

Looking back, I would say I had a happy childhood. When I wasn't at school, I would play around the farm with Yanis, my adorable younger brother. There were goats to milk and chickens to feed but mostly, often in glorious weather, we would take to the fields searching for snakes and lizards. Sometimes, we would take a back-pack and trek to the foothills of Mount Pentelikon in a quest to spy lammergeyers circling the thermals.

I remember sneaking into my Grandfather's study and delving into one of the pictorial books on Homer's Iliad or his Odyssey. Whenever I think back at those early days, I do so with a warm glow; it was a land of dreams far away from life's doldrums and upsets we often encounter as we enter puberty and adulthood. My father's death when I was fourteen was a devastating blow to my childhood idyll and I plunged into a depression that lasted for months. My school work suffered, but I came through it with the help of my mother who remained strong despite her terrible loss.

I did well at school and managed to combine the demands of studying with having a good social life. My friends wondered how I appeared to do so little revision and still do well in exams. I often came over as being precocious because I had a good head for details and could recall things that my classmates had forgotten. There was some jealousy but I never took advantage of my academic gifts; mostly, we got on well together and I would step back and let my friends take the leading role in play and sport - although, I was quite good at tennis.

In those early teenage years, I had the usual encounters with boys, all innocent and not going further than clumsy kisses and blushes but, those pleasing distractions, did not keep me too long away from my own personal ambitions. I am perhaps one of the few people who actually enjoy studying and asking questions that enable me to better comprehend the complexities and curiosities of the world. This, of course, started early on in my Grandfather's study. He would come and join me after his evening meal and would read to me Herodotus's history or stories about the Greek gods, and I would constantly interrupt him with my questioning. He was a kind and patient man.

I matriculated from school with good grades and I found myself in the strange position of what would be described today as being 'head-hunted'. I loved most subjects except for Maths and I was torn between studying history or biology at university but, shortly after my results were known, I had a phone call from Professor Tavoularis of the University of Athens asking me whether I had considered doing a degree in philosophy. I told him I hadn't, but he persuaded me to come and see him and discuss the possibility of doing so. Maybe it was to do with my inquisitive nature or perhaps Professor Tavoularis's charm but, thinking back, it was mostly to do with my adolescent conceit that led me to accept his offer. I quizzed Grandpa afterwards but he totally denied having anything to do with it as he didn't know anyone from the School of Philosophy any more.

During the next three years, my life continued to be blessed. I loved the rigour that philosophy brought to my life and how academia never halted at the door of the lecture theatre; it spilled over into the cafeteria and bars surrounding the university where we continued to discuss philosophical ideas with the aid of coffee by day and alcohol by night. I made many close friends, and we all felt privileged that we could cocoon ourselves away from the unhallowed world of paid work – at least for the time being. In the second year of the course, I decided to study Classical Greek Philosophy which included the Pre-Socratics, Plato, Aristotle and the Stoics. It was a good choice; I loved reading how the ancients constructed competing cosmologies in an age unknown to science; I also felt connected to their morality in terms of searching for the good in life and the dangers of hubris. This, of course, provided lots of inebriated discussions amongst my friends often through to the early hours of the morning. Overall, during our three year of study, we had a great time and the essays and exams did not detract from the thrill of being steeped in the spirit of high ideals and ideas. Time did not exactly stand still but, looking back, it seemed there were occasions when time faded away like an irrelevancy.

I left the university with a good honours degree. My tutor informed me that my final dissertation was particularly good despite it being controversial. Apparently, I had put forward a credible argument to support the hypothesis that feelings as defined by Plato's pleasures and pains are an essential element of rational thought. He informed me that some of the lecturers disagreed with the position I took, but most agreed I had argued my case extremely well. I came away from that meeting feeling exuberant which continued through to the next day when I met with the Dean of School. After more praise, he offered me the chance to teach at the university to the first year undergraduates, initially on a short term contract. I thanked him but something within me hesitated – I said I would consider his offer and let him know by the end of the week. Nevertheless, I walked out of that room imagining the rest of my life was laid out before me like some yellow-brick road to an Emerald City. But fate soon played its hand - that afternoon I received a phone call from mother saying Grandpa had died.

When I arrived home, he was still in his study with Herodotus open on his lap. His head was lowered as if he was reading, but the thing I noticed more than anything was the smile on his face. 'He's with Grandma now,' I remember my mother saying. I nodded, then went over and kissed his brow; together we laid him gently on the floor. The next day, Doctor Theo came round with the death certificate. He came with a stretcher and Yanis helped him put Grandpa into the funeral car. As the doors were gently shut, Doctor Theo whispered in my ear, inviting me to come and see him at his surgery later on that day. I went thinking it was about Grandpa but I soon discovered how wrong I could be. 'Did I know that Mrs Floros has lung cancer?' he asked quietly but formally. I shook my head and found I couldn't speak. He continued by telling me that she had been ill for over a year but she hadn't wanted me to know whilst I was doing my degree. He said he was aware that telling me was against my mother's wishes but he felt that now was the right time to do so. He seemed to be nervous and kept on repeating himself about it being the right time to tell me followed by his repeated assurance that he hadn't detected a worsening of her condition.

I came away from the surgery in a flurry of heightened emotions followed by a sense of anger of being the last person to know about her condition. When I got back to the house, I phoned the Dean immediately to say I could not accept the post with vague words about there being a death in the family. He was kind enough to say that the position was still open if I changed my mind. I thanked him but I was too much in shock to say more. Over the next few weeks, I wandered aimlessly about the farm in a depressed state. I said nothing to my mother and tried to put on a brave face whenever we talked, but she sensed something was wrong and kept on asking me if I was alright.

Over the next two months, I helped Yanis with jobs around the farm and Mama with preparing the evening meal, but I was restless and it proved difficult to hide my feelings. Yanis knew the reason for my low spirits which occasionally spilled over into irritability; eventually, he told me to go away and find myself again. He assured me he could manage the farm well enough on his own and would keep an eye on Mama at the same time.

'It's not as if she's at 'death's door'', he would say. 'She's quite capable of doing what she normally does around the farm and, beside, she has many friends in the neighbourhood to keep an eye on her.'

After much soul-searching and trying to overcome pangs of guilt, I eventually agreed with the assurance he would phone me if he sensed any change in Mama's condition. Three days later, I went away. My mother hugged me at the car door and told me to take care of myself and to keep in touch. Yanis shook my hand but then I flung my arms around him and whispered 'Thank you!'

I made my way back to Athens and stayed with my friend, Nadia. In the evenings, we drank Vermouth and talked about our happy days at the university. I remember how we got the giggles as we recounted the drunken exploits of ex-boyfriends and the peculiar habits and ticks of some of our lecturers. Each day, whilst Nadia went off to work as a receptionist, I would go hunting for a room of my own. As luck would have it, I found a flat in the same apartment block where I rented as an undergraduate, so I moved in on a short term contract. It was now early September and a new intake of students was coming into the city to take up residence before the start of their studies.

During the next few weeks I drifted; each morning, I would go to my favourite café on Solonos Street before strolling along to the university library where I refreshed my memory on the competing philosophies of Parmenides and Heraclitus. I remember on one evening, I went to see one of Aristophanes' comic plays in a theatre on Omonia Street. Occasionally, I went to a bar but most of my friends had already left to take up posts in the civil service or were doing casual work as they waited for life opportunities to come their way.

As I rose every day from my bed, I felt that I had to do something with my life but I couldn't shake off my malaise, and my mother would incessantly occupy my thoughts. I eventually did what people don't usually do in my predicament - I stopped going to the bars and drinking alcohol. Even though only a few months had lapsed since I was last in Athens, most people I knew had moved on; I was wise enough to know that you could not re-enact the past by drinking it into being.

In those weeks, I would phone my mother every morning. There was always a tension and our conversation was often stilted and awkward but, one day, I could tell from her voice that she knew that I knew about her cancer. Her voice was more relaxed and chirpy. I felt a great weight had been lifted. I remember thinking afterwards - maybe her cancer would go away; we are told that miracles *do* happen.

I went, as usual, to my favourite café on Solonos Street and drank my cappuccino in the warmth of the morning sun. In my relaxed state, I looked at the people passing by. There were all sorts: some of the women still wore light dresses and one or two men wore shorts. For some reason, my mind was drawn to their physical shape. I started counting and, during the length of my stay, found myself concluding there were many more weighty young people around compared with when I was a teenager. There and then, I decided to do some research. I went to the university library and came across a report that stated that over 40% of children in Greece were now considered to be either overweight or obese - that was staggering! I expected it to be that high elsewhere in the western world but not in Greece where natural produce is grown in abundance. I did more library research that week which reported similar findings. Each morning as I sipped coffee under the café awning, I confirmed my count. Athens had changed a lot over the last ten years. Back then, there were relatively few fast food outlets selling American-style food and drink; now, you couldn't go more than fifty paces without bumping into one!

One morning, while I was sipping and watching, I had a vision of Grandpa looking up from his book and giving me one of his big smiles. It was probably nothing more than my imagination playing tricks but, once the image faded, I instantly realised what I must do: I had to know what societal and psychological causes are behind so many young people being over-weight? I finished my coffee and went straight to the university where I searched the prospectus for suitable courses. There was a one year postgraduate course on promotional health. I phoned

Yanis to ask him what he thought of the idea and he said: 'Just do it!'.

That would have been the new direction I would have taken if it wasn't for me spotting something out of the corner of my eye as I was seated in the faculty office filling out an application form. On the notice board there was a poster which read: 'Erasmus Scholarship - The University of Manchester'. I read further and found that the philosophy department was looking for a European scholar for postgraduate study on 'Philosophy and Health'. In a flurry of excitement, I made a note of the details including the email address of a Doctor Pendlebury.

Looking back at the events that followed, I would say that there was an intensity of activity which lasted until I left Greece in January. Doctor Pendlebury emailed me back the very same day saying he was interested in my application and would let me know the outcome once he had contacted my tutor. The next day, he phoned and said he had accepted me for the scholarship based on my tutor's glowing recommendation. Initially, he informed me, the course would be for one year which would enable me to complete a Masters degree but it could be extended to two years for a doctorate depending on my progress.

I was over-the-moon! I phoned Mama and told her the news; she was delighted! That evening, I went out for a celebratory drink with Nadia and four other university friends. It was just like the old times, discussing philosophy and drinking too many Mythos Beers. The following morning, I found myself alone in Nadia's flat wondering how I got there!

In the weeks that followed there was plenty for me to do: I had to re-apply for a passport and there were a multitude of forms for me to complete in order for the Greek government to approve my scholarship. I went to live back at home for awhile and scurried about getting things ready whilst helping Yanis with odd jobs around the farm. Both he and mum were excited by my new adventure and they said it was the best thing that could have happened. Before I left, I went to see Doctor Theo who assured me that Mama's cancer was in remission based on the latest chest x-ray.

By early January, I had left the mild climate of the Mediterranean and was living in the frosty outskirts of Manchester. The day after I arrived, I took the tram into the city and went to buy some winter clothes from one of the big department stores. The next few days were spent doing mundane but necessary things such as enrolling at the university, opening a bank account, and registering with a doctor. I also needed to find out where the best independent shops were located so I could buy healthy food on a regular basis. On my travels, I was able to confirm that Manchester had the same problem as Athens – too many overweight people. Many of them could be seen eating junk food 'on the hoof' as they dashed to catch up with themselves between work and home.

By the second week, I had met up with Doctor Pendlebury, who gave me a quick tour of the department enabling me to shake hands with lots of people whose names I wouldn't remember. He showed me my desk in the postgraduate room and introduced me to my fellow postgraduates – at least, the ones who happened to be there at the time. The room had a high ceiling but, nevertheless, it had a good atmosphere and I could hear and smell the sound of coffee percolating in the small ante-room close by.

Later on that day, I had another meeting with Doctor Pendlebury so that we could chat about the scope of my research. He thought it would be a good idea if I centred my studies on Plato seeing that I already had a good grounding in his philosophy and I could probably use some of the research I had already done in my dissertation. This should provide a 'springboard' (Doctor Pendlebury's word) to assess health matters in the modern world. I asked him what I should concentrate on first? He uttered a low pitch humming noise and proceeded to twist and break one of his paperclips in half. Finally, he replied by saying it was up to me but suggested it would be a good idea if I wrote something about Plato's life in Greece in terms of a general introduction to the type of society he lived in followed up by his ideas on human anatomy and health.

I came away from Doctor Pendlebury's office feeling confused and a bit disheartened. He had an air of aloofness about him which didn't inspire me to be enthusiastic about what I was doing - as though he was only going through the motions. Over the next few weeks, usually whilst drinking coffee with fellow postgraduate students, I found that some of them shared the same view; although Simon, who was doing a doctorate on Popper, thought he was alright once you got to know him or, perhaps more importantly, once he got to know you.

In those early, dark days of January, I developed some sort of routine. I would take an early morning tram into Manchester, alight at St. Peter's Square, and then walk along Oxford Road to the university. It was a good walk and, by the time I got to my desk, I was ready for a warming cup of coffee. I was usually the first one there, so my first job was to get the percolator bubbling away. Some of my fellow researchers would usually arrive soon afterwards and, together, we would settle down, cups in hand, for our morning chat. It was Christiana and Morris who were the usual 'early birds' and so I got to know them better than the others. Most of the postgraduates would drift in late in the morning and there were some that I never saw at all. Morris informed me that some of the postgraduates did paid work during the day so they only came in during the evening and some of them even worked through the night.

During those dark mornings, we chatted about the freezing weather, or what was happening in the news, or about the perceived lack of progress in our research area, but inevitably, as the coffee was sipped dry, our thoughts would turn to the day ahead. Then we would rise up and make our way to our desks to delete superfluous emails, carry on writing up our projects, or go to the library to find something that could possibly help us along our solitary research paths. More often than not, I would go to the library in search of a book or research paper and then settle down in my usual seat on the second floor to make notes and to scribble down ideas. In the first three weeks, I had filled two notebooks and printed off lots of research papers but felt I was just collecting lots of thoughts rather than making any progress. One day in late January, I emailed Doctor Pendlebury in a state of panic; his reply was: 'Just write regardless of what comes out – revisions would come later on'. I must confess I felt much better about things after that and so I started to put pen to paper or, more accurately, finger to keyboard.

I made good progress and by the end of January, I had written the first part of the paper which described the political and social world that Plato would have known during the fourth and third centuries BC. Thoughts of war with Sparta and a political system supported by slaves would rattle around my head each morning as I walked along Oxford Road. As I gazed upon the unlit heaps of clothes and sleeping bags in the doorways, I couldn't reconcile these homeless people with the well-fed slaves in ancient Athens. I used to refer to these mounds as city moles although I knew, underneath those heaps of clothing, there were real people lost in a desolate Hades underworld unbeknown to the ancients. The daily commuters would either walk past them without giving them a second glance (or thought), or step around them on route to their over-sized breakfast from one of the fast food outlets. I tried to console myself by thinking that people living in ancient Greece were more likely to die in battle or from diseases such as typhoid but, nevertheless, there was something psychological disturbing about these bundles of grey next to crumpled-up drink cartons and plastic bags containing bits of food and a spattering of possessions. I tried to think what Plato would say about them but no inspiration came my way, although, in my imagination, I often thought that Grandpa was trying to tell me something of great importance.

One morning, I gave ten pounds to a teenage girl who was visually shivering with cold and told her to get some hot soup and a cup of tea. This particular event became the talking point for our 'early bird' discussion group. Christiana, whose research area was to do with Isaiah Berlin's concept of freedom, thought that the state should do more to look after these people by providing them with opportunities to get out of extreme poverty. Morris, who was influenced by the American pragmatists, disagreed. It was all to do with choice and, although most of these people came from broken homes, it was up to them either to stay in poverty or to make the choice to improve their lot - there was nothing stopping them from breaking away from the shackles of drink and drugs if they wanted to. Both Christiana and I said his stance was too harsh as there were mental health issues to consider and, most importantly, we should think of them as fellow humans who need our help. Then I put forward the argument I had written in my dissertation; I said Plato urges us to regard feelings as being a part of rational thought and it is our duty to reach out to people who cannot help themselves. Morris didn't agree but, by then, we had finished our coffees and were mentally sorting out our work priorities for the day.

For my part, that particular day was a write-off. As I sat in my usual place in the library with my laptop in front of me, I couldn't get that girl out of my mind - she looked so scared. I kept trying to console myself by asking what Plato would say or do, but the thought that reverberated was that there were some issues that remain unresolved. In some of his dialogues, he would have Socrates and his friends walking away into the warmth of the afternoon sun knowing that they hadn't achieved a satisfactory conclusion on a particular moral topic. This was aporia, an impasse, and no further discussion on that particular day would resolve things. But, I didn't think that was the case with our morning discussion - we just ran out of time. Perhaps Morris would have come round to a more compassionate conclusion given more time to discuss the problem. But the whole episode niggled me. There must be something society could do or, more importantly, what I could do to alleviate the suffering of these homeless people in some way.

As I was doodling in my notebook, I came to a resolution. There were hundreds of homeless people on the streets of Manchester and it would be impossible for me to help everyone I met on my commute. The utilitarian argument of trying to create the greatest happiness of the greatest number of people was not only unconvincing but far beyond my means to make any inroads into the problem. Instead, I decided to help one person – that girl. So from then on, whenever I saw her as I passed by on my way to and from the university, I would give her any loose change I had in my pocket. Over the coming months, she gained my trust, and we became friends. Eventually, I was able to help her in ways I did not think possible.

Since coming to Manchester, I used to phone home every week. Yanis usually reported that Mama still seemed to have a lot of energy even though she spent more time napping in the afternoon - which she referred to as 'her Greek siesta'. Doctor Theo also confirmed she was doing well whenever I phoned; the cancer still seemed to be in remission.

By early February, the crisp, cold days of the city had been replaced by rain which persisted throughout the month. Morris informed me that Manchester was one of the wettest places in the country and I should expect rain to fall on average three days out of five - I didn't believe him. Yanis phoned me one rainy day with descriptions of Mount Pentelikon looking beautiful in the snow and people actually skating on Lake Marathon. On that occasion, I felt the pangs of homesickness strongly, but I didn't let it affect my research. I plodded on with my routine and, by the end of February, I had completed the section on Plato's human anatomy and health. All I had to do then was the conclusion and go through it one more time looking for grammatical errors.

I sent the finished document off to Doctor Pendlebury and went to see him three days later expecting the worst. I remember him flicking through the sheets of paper in an unnerving silence. Then, with a nod of his head and a semblance of a smile, he looked up and declared that it was on the right lines and would serve as part of my introductory chapter. He thought the way I had compared and contrasted Plato's pre-scientific ideas on health with the medical advancements of our modern world was particularly good. However, he thought I needed to put more emphasis on explaining how the rigid social order in ancient Greece restricted people's understanding of human anatomy and the causes of disease. He asked me to do some more research on how the ruling elite at the time thought that surgery and hands-on healing was synonymous with manual operations and, therefore, inferior to their own intellectual understanding. The upshot, he said, was that commonly accepted, non-empirical ideas in ancient Greece created a straight jacket of thinking that would stymie the advancements in medical science for centuries to come.

He advised me not to revise what I had written at this stage but to work on the main body of the thesis. I followed his advice. The first draft of my introductory chapter (with notes and references) can be found at the back of this book under the title 'Plato's World'.

In Search of the Mean

During March, I continued with my routine of going to the university early. My morning commute was becoming easier as the spring equinox drew closer and the days grew longer, although, everywhere was still sodden. Rain had fallen persistently for six weeks and the streets had permanent puddles on them with no where to go. I read there was serious flooding in Yorkshire and the Lake District.

Our early bird discussion group still continued as we tried to put the world to right over a morning cup of coffee, and I got to know them better as the weeks went by. Christiana, who was from Utrecht, told me the most intimate things and seemed to want to tell me everything there was to know about her love life and her tendency to love women as much as she did men. She informed me that her mother was an ex-nun who fell in love with her father, an artist, who had ended up in jail after counterfeiting several Dutch masterpieces. They were now living happily together in a mobile home somewhere in the Netherlands. She also told me about her passion for hedgehogs. She was one of the founding members of the Hedgehog Protection League and enthused away at having a hedgehog wintering over in the hibernation box in her back garden.

Morris, on the other hand, was less forthcoming than Christiana. Eventually, in dribs and drabs, bits of his life history came out. His home was in Oxfordshire; his father was in the insurance business and his mother had been a teacher but was now confined to a wheelchair having succumbed to Multiple Sclerosis. He had a refined accent that portrayed his education at Eton and at Oxford; but first impressions often belie someone's true nature. He sometimes came across as a bit of a know-all but, gradually, I tapped into his sensitivity and kindness.

After we had finished our coffees and gone our separate ways, I would gravitate to my usual seat on the second floor of the library. Doctor Pendlebury suggested I should find all I could about Plato's concept of the mean for my next chapter, and so I read all the relevant bits from Jowett's 'The Dialogues of Plato' and managed to fill another notebook in the process. I developed the habit of cutting out articles from newspapers and sticking them in a scrapbook so I could relate my research to current health issues. Most of them were about over-indulgence with fear-ladened headlines such as: 'More than three bottles of wine per week can cause liver failure in women'; 'Diabetes could cost you 10 years' and 'Obesity linked to seven million new illnesses'. The one I liked the most was: 'Coffee may stave off heart disease'. I had only a vague notion at the time as to how these cuttings were going to help me in writing my thesis.

After I had spent several hours sitting in the library, what usually happened was my mind would begin to wander. As I looked out of the window at the rain-charged sky, I would occasionally question what I was doing there; research could be so debilitating. Yes, I got to know Morris and Christiana well but, even with them, genuine conversation was sometimes stilted by the need to plough our own research furrow, and Doctor Pendlebury did not exactly fill me with great enthusiasm.

Then, there were the other postgraduates. When I spoke to any of them, they were nice enough but conversations were often framed according to their own research area. Once a month, we were obliged to come together as a seminar group and one of us would present a paper on what we were doing, and invite questions from the audience. Members of staff were not usually there; the whole experience seemed contrived and it didn't seem to help any of us with our individual projects apart from ideas about research methods. I couldn't help comparing this dull academic routine to my days in Athens where lasting friendships were forged beyond the lecture room in the cafeterias and bars.

Despite these misgivings, I plodded on with my research. Doctor Pendlebury seemed happy enough with my progress when I saw him at the end of March. He thought I had enough material from my notebooks to start writing the next chapter; I wondered whether his lukewarm response was a peculiar sort of enthusiasm but, if it was, it didn't inspire me to write anything significant. I had developed a writer's block but couldn't put my finger on what was the reason for it. Mama seemed to be doing well whenever I phoned home and, by April, the rain had stopped and the sun was shining on the streets of Manchester. The spring flowers were in bloom and the trees started to paint the cityscape with dabs of green.

Another distraction was the girl. As the weather improved, she was no longer a grey shape in a dark entrance, I was able to have conversations with her. Sometimes, I would take her into a nearby café and we would have longer chats. She told me her name was Lisa and had been living on the streets for seven months. Unlike most homeless people, she came from a well-to-do home in Wilmslow and had gone to a private school. Bit by bit, I got to know more about her family life. She painted a picture of her mother as being sensitive and kind. In contrast, her father was bombastic and bullying who didn't allow her to bring friends into the home and outdoor activities had to be approved as being worthy of their social standing.

During the first few meetings, I let her talk freely and I would nod my head and listen. Eventually, as her confidence grew, I started to ask more searching questions. I asked her why she thought her father had treated her so unkindly? After some hesitation, she recounted what her mother had told her. Her father believed she was not his daughter. Apparently, her mother had come home from an Open University summer school and shortly afterwards became pregnant with Lisa. He couldn't get it out of his head that his wife hadn't had an affair, and so, there developed a permanent rift between husband and wife, and father and child.

Lisa went on to tell me how he became more dismissive and controlling as she grew older. If the house appeared to be untidy or his evening meal was not on time, he would become annoyed and sometimes angry. Lisa's mum would react by getting agitated causing her to drop plates and other things, which would result in him calling her hurtful, derogatory names.

Occasionally though, he could be quite charming but, despite these rare attempts of trying to be something that he really wasn't, it didn't take long for him to revert back to type with his angry moods and cutting criticisms. When he was at home, daughter and mother would tip-toe around the house on eggshells but their long lasting suffrage drew them closer together, giving one another emotional support against his snide remarks and bullying tactics. The best time of all was when he wasn't around and then they would go shopping together. Lisa told me there were pockets of freedom when he worked late or on those Saturdays when he went to the office. There was never anything to do in the house so, when the weather allowed, they went walking along the country trails around Wilmslow. Her mum bought her a pair of binoculars and they had fun identifying the local birds and butterflies.

All this and more besides, I gathered over several weeks, but she never gave any explanation as to what events had caused her to leave her luxury home for the streets of Manchester. I asked her once but she clammed up and mumbled something about her mum being lost. I decided not to pursue it any further but to wait until she was ready to tell me.

Despite the dire circumstances she had found herself in, she appeared to be both resilient and resolute. She had survived the first winter on the streets and managed to huddle up with other homeless people during the long, cold nights. She told me she was getting street-wise, and got to know who she could trust and who to avoid. So far, she had not been assaulted in any way. She said she was sometimes hungry but people gave generously and there were always the food banks to fall back on. The main problem was something I didn't expect - a shortage of sanitary products. From then on, I ensured she had a regular supply.

April had come and gone, and I had nothing to show for my efforts apart from being on my fourth book of notes and having a scrapbook of newspaper cuttings on health issues. I also had a pile of journal papers I had printed out and several electronic attempts of trying to start my next chapter. Looking back, one of the reasons for my lack of progress was that I had too much information and felt too unsettled to filter it in any coherent way.

The eventful day came in early May. I was seated in my usual place in the library with my laptop and notes before me. I remember looking at the chapter title; the words 'Plato's Concept of the Mean' glared back at me. Then, I read again the introductory paragraph. At the final full stop, and not knowing what next to write, I went round again, first looking at the title and then re-reading until ending up at the same full stop; a loop which I had been round, at least, for the last twenty minutes.

'It's not as though I don't know anything about the subject matter,' I said to myself.

After staring blankly at the page and then letting my mind drift on to thinking about Mama and then Lisa, I said to myself - 'To Hell with it!' I gathered up my books and papers with the view to having a coffee and then coming back to it later. As I was pushing them into my bag, I heard a 'ping' from my laptop indicating an email has just arrived. Thinking it was from Doctor Pendlebury, I opened it up to find it was from someone called Aristocles. The message read: 'I believe you are having a few problems with your latest chapter. I think I can help. Meet me at Queen Victoria's statue in Piccadilly Gardens in thirty minutes and we'll discuss things over a cup of coffee.'

I had no idea who Aristocles was and how he got hold of my email address; and how did he know I was having problems with writing my chapter? I hesitated but, despite my anxiety, I emailed back saying I would be there.

I stepped out of the university library into the early warmth of the day, with bright white clouds set in a blue sky. In the quad, the birds were chirruping and several students were lounging on the grass chatting away and soaking up the sun. On Oxford Street there was more of a rush but people seemed to be enjoying the sun's warmth as they paced out.

'I wonder whether this Aristocles guy is someone Doctor Pendlebury knows?' I pondered as I threaded my way down the street, and then I thought: 'Perhaps, I shouldn't have agreed to meet him ... He could be anyone ... a charlatan, a fraudster, or maybe a rapist!'

I continued with this internal monologue as I walked on. 'What would Mama think about me meeting a complete stranger!' And then, as the rhythm of my strides set in, I consoled myself by saying to myself: 'No harm can come of it ... it's not as if it's night-time!'

I turned right up Portland Street and then proceeded along it until I reached the tramlines that border Piccadilly Gardens. I soon arrived at the black statue of Queen Victoria where the pigeons were trying their best to turn it white. Seated on the steps was a bearded old man twiddling with a rainbow coloured walking-stick. As soon as I came into view, he raised himself up and came towards me.

'Allow me to introduce myself,' he said, with a nod of his head. 'My name is Aristocles.'

'Pleased to meet you, I'm Alecta,' I replied hesitantly. 'Your email gave me quite a shock as if you know me!'

'I know who you are,' he answered enigmatically. 'I'm here to help!'

'How do you know I need help? Not even my tutor

knows I'm struggling to write up my latest chapter!'

'I need to explain ... '

'I assume you have acquired some personal details about me from the university? Has Doctor Pendlebury asked you to get in touch with me?'

'Not exactly,' he replied vaguely. 'As you can see, I am old; I lectured once at one of the ancient Greek universities. Let's just say I've had plenty of teaching experience with research students like you.'

'Which university are you from?'

'Athens - the same as you!'

I glared at him in disbelief but, before I could reply, he said: 'There's a nice café just round the corner on Market Street. We can chat there for as long as we want and I'll answer all your questions!'

He led the way through the square and across the tramlines where pigeons pecked at bits of sandwich and pizza - remnants from the fast food outlets around the square. Once inside, he directed me to a quiet corner table where he left me looking after his rainbow stick whilst he went to the counter with an order for two cappuccinos. On his return, he sat opposite, stirring his coffee and staring at me with his blue eyes.

'Well! ... Where do you fit into the scheme of things?' I enquired. 'You must be Greek with a name like that, but it's so old-fashioned! Nobody is called Aristocles these days.'

'I suppose you need some kind of explanation,' he replied, in a furtive manner. 'I cannot tell you everything straight away but you must believe me when I say I am here to help. I have a real interest in your topic from an academic point of view. Perhaps we can start by giving me some idea of where you are up to in your writing and the problems you've encountered so far. After which, I can tell you everything you need to know about myself.'

I gave him a puzzled look not knowing whether to trust him or not, but I decided to give him the benefit of the doubt - at least, for the time being. 'Alright then,' I answered cautiously. 'My main objective is to make Plato's ideas more palatable to a modern audience. I am interested in how his views on health are still relevant today. One of my problems is trying to incorporate some of his not so good ideas on health.'

'Such as?'

'Well, he didn't have a very good understanding of anatomy and how diseases take hold. But from what I have read so far, he seemed to have a reasonable grasp of how imbalances of elementary chemicals can cause ill-health and make people age prematurely.'

'That is so,' Aristocles replied, sipping his cappuccino. 'But we cannot be too hard on him. He lived in an age where science was in its infancy. They had no-one coming along to show them how to perceive the natural world differently. There was no scientific know-how to guide them and so the early Greek academics reasoned by means of analogy, an approach that often led them astray. They also believed that mathematics was god-given; that is why Plato described the workings of the human body in terms of mathematical proportionality.'

'I've read about that in his Timaeus; how the four elements of fire, air, earth and water need to be in proportion in order to sustain life. But what I'm trying to write about in this current chapter is how Plato's concept of proportionality has a wider meaning in terms of how people should live their lives to make them feel better and, hopefully, to make them better people.'

Aristocles took a noisy but thoughtful sip of his coffee before continuing: 'As you know, Plato was mostly concerned about how people *ought* to live their lives. Socrates was his inspiration here. Proportionality developed into the broader notion of the mean as a kind of standard with which to compare people who live their lives in an extreme way. Plato made the distinction between necessary pleasures that enhance health, and those that are unnecessary, usually associated with over-indulgence. Therefore, living in the mean is all to do with being aware of what pleasures are necessary for good living.'

As he continued talking, my mind drifted and I found myself gazing around at the people in the café; I was aware of young people with extended waistlines - just like I had observed in Athens. I found myself saying: 'Plato wrote a lot about the over-indulgence of Athenian men.'

'Yes, he did,' he replied. 'I have a clear image in my mind, during the third century BC, of hordes of revellers taking to the streets in the early hours of the morning after a heavy drinking session at the symposium. Plato's frustrations were mainly directed at young, aristocratic men who lived in indolence and luxury. In the Republic, he wrote about them derogatively as being bloated with waters and winds, and referred to them collectively as - Tyrannical Man.'

'Nowadays, he would come across another creature - Tyrannical Woman!' I remarked light-heartedly. 'Women can be just as bad as men. You'll see lots of unseemly behaviour here on Saturday nights. Drugs and alcohol go a long way to fuel out-of-control behaviour.'

Aristocles looked up with a quizzical look on his face.

'You amaze me when you say that women can be as bad as men. Is this true? In my day, the women stayed at home and were responsible for the household and the rearing of children. Naturally, there were occasional lapses but, when that happened, family and friends would come together to help get the woman in question on the road to recovery. It was mainly the men who were the problem, in my day.'

'You keep on saying 'in my day'. You sound as if you don't know much about the modern world ... Where do you come from?'

He hesitated before answering as if he was hiding something. ' ... I come from a small village called Frosyni, in northern Greece. It is very remote and we are not caught up with events in the modern world. To a great extent, village life is the same now as what it was in Plato's day.'

'Maybe you do come from a remote village in Greece, but even in the remotest places, everyone's connected globally by means of the internet!'

Aristocles gave out a big sigh. 'Unfortunately, that's not true for me. Where I come from there are few ways of knowing what is going on in this world.'

'You must be able to, otherwise, how do you keep your knowledge of things up-to-date? ... and besides, you emailed me, didn't you?'

'That was ... an exceptional occurrence,' he replied hesitantly, stirring the froth on his cappuccino. 'Believe me, when I say it is difficult for me to keep in touch with worldly news.'

'It may have been an exceptional occurrence but you *did* contact me by email. Where did you get my email address from? Was it from my tutor, Doctor Pendlebury?'

'No ... not your tutor ... I suppose I better tell you the truth, but it may come as a bit of a shock ... I knew your Grandfather!'

I looked hard and long at this old man who had just forced himself into my life. 'You can't have!' I said vehemently.

'We were great friends,' he said, with a gentle smile on his face. 'We met on a philosophy course at Athens when we were young and we've been great friends ever since. We used to have a reunion ever so often, usually over coffee in one of the city cafés. The last time I met up with him was a month before he died. He made me promise to keep an eye on you once he was unable to do so himself.'

'I'm not sure I believe you! He never told me anything about you when he was alive so why should I believe you now?'

'You can believe me or not. It's up to you ... You must make up your own mind ... It was your Grandpa who gave me your email address. Believe me when I say - I knew him like a brother and I was deeply upset to hear that he'd died.'

'If you knew him that well, why didn't you come to his funeral, and why doesn't the family know anything about you?'

'I had good reasons why I couldn't come to the funeral, which I can't explain right now, but ... Michal, your Grandfather, was a good friend to me and I miss him dearly.'

I looked into his blue eyes trying to search for the truth. I was impressed that he knew my Grandfather's name but I still didn't believe he was telling me the whole story or, perhaps, what he was telling me was true as far as it went. I sensed there was something he was holding back.

He smiled gently at me and seemed to be reading my mind. 'If you don't trust me as to my true identity then simply regard me as a harmless, elderly scholar from an old Greek University who has made a lifelong study of Plato, who wants to share his knowledge with a fellow researcher - which is you. We can help one another. I can aid you in acquiring a better understanding of Plato's original ideas whilst you can help me assess how relevant his philosophy is in the world today ... Is that agreed?'

'Ok, it's agreed.' I replied tentatively. 'But I'm uncertain as to whether you are who you say you are. Is your name really Aristocles?'

'It is! You must blame my mother and father for that!'

I smiled at his attempt to set me at my ease. He had a re-assuring nature even though I didn't fully trust his motives for helping me. 'Ok, I won't ask you any more questions, at least for the time being,' I said boldly. 'Your acquaintance with Grandpa is convincing. It's just like him to find ways of helping me, even after his death!'

'I'm so pleased we can work together!' he exclaimed, with a tap of his rainbow stick on the wooden floor. 'We can learn from one another and hopefully have fun at the same time!'

' ... And maybe I can report back to my tutor that I'm making good progress on my chapter.'

'Good! ... Well, let's get started,' he said, eagerly rubbing his hands together. 'But I think we'll need another coffee before we start.'

I volunteered to get two more cappuccinos and, on

returning, I took out my notebook and pen. As I looked at his dishevelled white hair and beard, I couldn't stop myself from thinking that he looked a lot like Plato as portrayed by the painting in Grandpa's study.

'So, let's get our thinking heads on,' he said, stirring his coffee. 'Correct me if I'm wrong, but didn't you say you were currently writing about Plato's idea on proportionality?'

'Yes, but I'm more interested in how it relates to people's lives, especially in terms of what Plato wrote about proportionality in association with the mean. I've already come up with a diagram to illustrate the concept - a bit like a statistical distribution.'

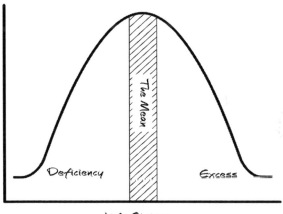

Life Choices

At that point, I opened up my notebook and drew a quick sketch. 'As you can see, there are three distinct areas associated with people's life choices. Plato was never against people abstaining from having pleasures but he was totally opposed to people being enslaved by them.'

'I assume that enslavement comes about when someone stays too long in the outer zones of your diagram,' Aristocles interrupted.

Yes, that's correct. He reminds us that in seeking out pleasurable experiences we cannot hope to avoid pain in the process. Plato's answer to this is - we must seek for a balance between pleasure and pain by living our lives in the mean. Hopefully, our rational minds will keep us there otherwise pain will accompany pleasures if we stray too long in the outer zones. So, for example, if we take Tyrannical Man with his binge drinking and eating, he would be firmly placed in the excess area.'

'The same goes for Tyrannical Woman, I suppose!' added Aristocles smilingly.

'Yes. That's true,' I replied, smiling too. 'It is fair to say that over-indulgence can result in such people becoming more and more unhealthy not only in body but in mind. Plato would say, I think, that a person becomes enslaved by irrational desires to the extent that the mind loses control over what's best for them.'

'I agree ... But what about on the deficiency side?'

'The same goes for that as well, although, Plato only seems to have written about deficiency in relation to bodily exhaustion on those occasions when there is insufficient intake of food and drink. Of course, that's also true today; you'll find lots of homeless people living on the city streets who are without the bare necessities of warmth and sustenance. However, there is another group of people who are under-nourished for other reasons even though there's plenty of food around for them to eat. They are usually young people, females mostly, although males can be subject to this, who develop a false image about their bodies and, as a result, starve themselves to the point that they can easily die.'

'Why would they want to do that?' Aristocles enquired, sounding concerned. 'In Plato's day, there were women who refused to eat when bad things happened in their lives, such as the loss of a child. Are these people like this, or are they starving themselves even though there are no tragedies in their lives?'

'It's hard to tell in all cases but they're more likely to belong to the latter group,' I replied. 'It's a psychological condition which comes under the general name of anorexia. Some of these young people have a distorted view of their body image and see themselves as fat, even though their bones are showing through their flesh. Some of them are so driven that they join a cult with other anorexics on the internet. They convince themselves that what they're doing is the right way to live. Some of them even think themselves as part of a religion worshipping a female goddess called Ana.'

Aristocles slowly nodded his head as he listened and seemed saddened by what he heard. 'I can understand why some people would want to end their lives when something terrible happens, but it seems to me that what you're describing are people risking their lives for no reason other than a desperate drive to seek attention from other people of a similar persuasion.'

'You may be right,' I replied. 'It probably more complicated than that. There could be something they're born with which is then triggered by a distressing event or trauma. But no matter what the cause, these young people are unhappy and they need help.'

'They certainly need help, for their souls are at risk,' said Aristocles sombrely.

'Why do you say that?'

'As you are aware, people in Plato's time believed in reincarnation; their deeds and misdeeds determined what they came back as in the next life. Maybe these anorexics are suffering from something that happened in their previous lives. It is not for me to judge. However, for the sake of this discussion, let's not get too involved in the afterlife just yet. Let's assume the concept of soul is the same as the mind, which is what Plato does in several of his dialogues. In that way, we can talk about mind and soul as being interchangeable. When I say that anorexic people risk their souls, I also mean it in the context of them losing their minds. Plato would say - extreme desires corrupt the soul. People can get to the stage in their lives where they no longer have the will to think rationally and are not able to help themselves. I reluctantly agree that some people who constantly crave for something can have fleeting satisfactions, however, I believe they have no enduring calm and contentment.'

I pondered what Aristocles said as I drank my coffee. 'So craving can occur even though people are under-nourished which appears to be a tautology,' I replied, trying to relate Aristocles views on Plato to my own research. 'I suppose what Plato is saying is that craving is in the mind regardless of whether someone is anorexic or over-indulging.'

Aristocles nodded his head. 'Plato believed that the body is an endless source of trouble to us and, even when we think we're enjoying ourselves, extreme pleasures can soon bring on pain and disease.'

'He was a bit of a doom and gloom merchant, wasn't he?'

'I think he was in a way,' he replied, having another sip of his cappuccino. 'I suppose he was mostly concerned about the consequences for someone's soul if they continue on a downward path. He wrote a lot about how diseases take hold in circumstances where extreme pleasures evoke excessive pains. He wrote that the worst of these diseases occurs when the soul (or, if you prefer – the mind) is driven by uncontrollable passions to the extent that the end result is madness!'

'Judging from our discussion, I suppose some anorexics would fit in that category. Although in today's society it is difficult to write about certain groups of people without upsetting them. The same goes for people who hold different religious points of view. That's one of the problems I have when I try and write about Plato's ideas in a modern setting.'

'As long as you write about things objectively, there shouldn't be any problems,' Aristocles replied encouragingly. 'But let's get back to the task in hand. If you look at the diagram you've drawn, I think we're too harsh on the people already living in the mean. There must be some room in there for experimentation and for people learning from their mistakes. I think the diagram should be re-drawn.

Aristocles took hold of my notebook and sketched another diagram.

'I see what you've done,' I commented. 'You've given more wiggle-room for people in the mean.'

'Wiggle-room is a strange expression but I think I understand. People are not restricted by a small range of alternatives. If you look at the horizontal axis, there are now more choices associated with the mean and they can all be beneficial to one's life. Having a broader mean suggests that a person goes through a learning process, often by trail and error, to find out which life choices are best for them. It's not just about people being penalised when they go astray, it is more about them knowing what's best for them on their life's journey, and this entails making mistakes and learning from them.'

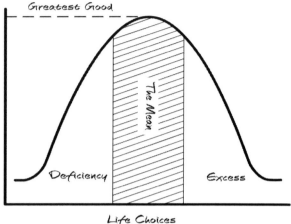

Life Choices

'Know Thyself,' I remarked, recalling what I had recently read. 'Plato's assumption is that no-one can be wise unless they know themselves first.'

'Yes, that's true,' replied Aristocles. 'In his early writing, he also has Socrates saying 'virtue is knowledge' which makes it imperative to go on a moral journey of self-discovery so that we become more morally astute as we come to know ourselves better and begin to make better choices for ourselves.'

'So, we cannot be wise unless we are prepared to become morally improved by our own actions?'

'Plato would say that wisdom is the ultimate aim of going on a moral journey,' he replied. 'But, it doesn't happen all at once. A person may still stray into the outer zones but hopefully they will learn from any mistakes made. He also writes that a variety of experiences can bring about a more pleasurable and healthier life, which indicates there is room for experimentation and learning about new modes of living without any permanent harm being done. Plato was well aware of our humanness. Anyone is capable of over-doing things. The problems arise over longer periods when we live too long in one or other of those outer zones.'

'Do these people suffer from a weakness of will so that they do not know what they are doing, or do they know what they are doing but continue to do harm to themselves anyway?' I asked.

Aristocles became quiet as he thought about what I had said. 'That is a very important question,' he eventually replied, stroking his beard. 'This is something that has been discussed by philosophers since philosophy came into being. In the Protagoras, Plato would answer it by saying that no-one goes willingly towards something that is bad for them, although they can be deceived into thinking that their bad habit is doing them good.'

'So how do people get back into the mean if they are reluctant to help themselves?' I asked.

'I can tell you what Plato would recommend, but first, tell me what happens in this society?'

I sipped my coffee whilst I sifted through my thoughts. 'It depends,' I finally said. 'The people we're talking about can't help themselves to begin with because they are so entrenched in their bad habits. The answer lies in other people helping them with encouragement and advice. Although, it seems to me that nothing is likely to help these people unless they are ready to accept that help.'

'So, what you're saying is that you can't force help

onto people, it's up to them to decide when they are ready for it. This assumes they have reached the stage where they know what damage is being done to them by continuing with their detrimental life style. Eventually, they come to understand the meaning of the term 'Know Thyself', and then they are willing to change their life habits by accepting help from other people.'

'Yes, I think so. We have many self-help groups, charities and other organisations which encourage people to stop drinking alcohol, or eating too much, or taking drugs. There is an abundance of doctors and dietary professionals giving advice on the best remedies including recommended diets and medicines. I assume something like that was happening in Plato's day?'

'Some of what you've described is familiar,' he replied. 'The physicians and other people would be guided by Hippocrates in giving medical advice and administering natural medicine, but there would be community pressure on these people as well. You must remember that Athens and other city-states needed to be on their guard against armed aggression and so they required their citizens to be ready to take up arms in defence of their city. It was, therefore, thought wrong for individuals to hide themselves away for long periods of time as this was thought to be harmful to the whole community. Plato also said that private living, away from the community, eventually brings about ill-health. This is why he put forward the idea that public meals were essential for community morale, which implied that citizens had to eat and drink under the watchful eye of one another.'

'Wouldn't the people feel resentful by the way the community put pressure on them?' I asked. 'It seems to me that coercion may undermine what we said earlier about people finding their own way back into the mean with the help of sympathetic people.'

'I think we have been pushed off course with our discussion which isn't a bad thing in itself,' replied Aristocles. 'But before we return to the main point, I would like to say that, despite good intentions, there will always be people in society who do not, cannot, change the way they behave regardless of how much help they receive, which means they are likely to be faced with some kind of corrective punishment imposed by their community.'

'So there will always be people who cannot be helped and remain forever outside the mean?'

I wouldn't put it that strongly,' Aristocles replied. 'Some of these people may take several life-times to realise where they've gone wrong. Remember what we discussed about people going on a moral journey? People cannot change what they are unless it comes from within, which means they need to have the rational will to want to change their lives for the better.'

'What you're saying seems to suggest that reincarnation is commonly regarded as being true,' I said, with a shake of my head. 'The general view today is there's no such thing unless you are a follower of one of the eastern religions such as Hinduism and Buddhism.'

'I don't know much about those religions, but what I would say is that reincarnation is a concept that was widely believed by the ancient Greeks. However, I think we must leave this important topic for another time,' he replied, gazing at me with his deep blue eyes. 'Let us stay with the notion of the mean. The main point is that people must be willing to change their lives for the better. They must want to transform their lives because that's the decision they've reached for themselves.'

'Which seems to suggest they must eventually find their way back into the mean because the alternatives outside of it are too unbearable?' I said.

'Yes, that's true, but don't let's get ourselves too tied up with the negative reasons for wanting to be in the mean. What's more important are the benefits that the mean brings to a person's life. As you can see at the top of the diagram, I have written 'The Greatest Good'. This is the reward for people living their life in the mean - they become wiser, more fulfilled, and hopefully happier.'

'It looks as though we're into Plato's theory of forms now that you've added the term 'good' to the discussion,' I replied. 'As you know, he would say the greatest good in life is only attainable through rational insight and wisdom.'

'Of course!' exclaimed Aristocles rather loudly, causing the couple on the next table to look up suddenly. 'You can't avoid talking about the theory of forms whenever you discuss the ethical aspects of Plato's philosophy. Concepts such as goodness and truth can't be found by relying on other people's opinions. When you are attuned to 'The Greatest Good', it transforms the whole of your life!'

'I remember reading in the Philebus how Plato has Socrates putting forward reasons why the greatest good is attributed to wisdom rather than pleasures of the body. He would say bodily pleasures are fleeting and often lead to pain whereas when someone searches for the good they become more fulfilled and there is every chance of achieving contentment in life.'

'That is well recounted,' he replied. 'As we've already pointed out, 'virtue is knowledge' which motivates us to search for a better and contented life. Plato also writes in the Philebus that the mean is where you find beauty, symmetry and truth. All of these are good reasons for staying in the mean.'

I thought about what had been said as I stirred my cappuccino. The conversation had become conceptual and a reoccurring thought crossed my mind - who was this aged scholar who appeared to know so much about Plato's philosophy? I suddenly decided to test his knowledge: 'Socrates writes that a return to the mean is a source of natural pleasure which is where the necessary pleasures reside. Do you think we can say that necessary pleasures are the same as natural pleasures?'

' ... I think we could say they are same,' he replied cautiously. 'But before we can come to any conclusion, it would be useful to discuss this further in the manner of Plato's dialectic by examining and cross-examining what we both think about natural and unnatural pleasures. What are your thoughts on this?'

I felt the onset of panic now that he had put me on the spot, as if he knew that I was trying to test him. Nothing came to mind immediately, so I looked around at the people in the café hoping for inspiration. I was aware of the variety of shapes and sizes, and most of them seemed to be relaxed as they conversed and drank their beverages. The thought that came into my mind was: 'Happiness is being in the moment', but I couldn't relate this to our discussion.

I looked at Aristocles drinking his coffee. 'What you are drinking is natural,' I said automatically. 'It is made of ground coffee beans and the milk from a cow. So you could say it is a natural product even though they have used a special percolating machine to make it. I would say, it is a natural drink but is it a necessary one?'

Aristocles nodded his head then looked beyond me in a kind of blank stare; he seemed to mutter something to himself. It was only when we regained eye contact that he replied: 'Plato would say that replenishment is required to sustain a healthy life. But we need to ask the question whether extra cups of coffee are necessary for this to happen? I've been looking at that sign over there on the wall which reads: 'Let every sense be seduced every time'. I'm thoroughly enjoying this coffee but if I am seduced to having another one then my enjoyment may turn to pain with the onset of indigestion. Eventually, if I continue to be seduced, my mind would become overwhelmed with the desire to drink more coffee. So, my mind has to be vigilant to keep check that I'm not drinking too much. My senses may be driving me to have another coffee but, hopefully, this temptation is checked by my rational thoughts weighing up the consequences.'

'I agree, but the problem arises when people don't always know the consequences of their actions or, more insidiously, they think they are behaving rationally when they're not. Remember what Plato wrote about the elderly Athenian statesmen? Over many years, they regularly acquired rich food and wine from the finest purveyors in Athens until eventually they became corpulent and unwell. But instead of blaming themselves, they blamed their advisers and trainers for giving them wrong advice as to what regimen they should be following whilst still over-indulging on those rich foods and wine. They were in denial as well as being ignorant of the main cause of their troubles.'

'That is a good example to illustrate your point,' Aristocles replied. 'It also reminds me what Plato said about children's desires. He described a thought experiment where a cook and a physician enter a competition as to which type of food is best to eat, with children acting as judges. It's a joke because he says that the children would kill the physician rather than the cook because they would always choose food that was tasty but bad for them rather than the physician's choice of healthy, wholesome food which is not so appealing.'

'It seems that Plato has a sense of humour!'

'Of course! We cannot assume he was always serious-minded just because his speciality was philosophy,' Aristocles replied, with a smile on his face.

'I think he used humour to put a particular point across, but who knows what he was like in real life? We can only use our imagination.'

Aristocles had a glint in his eye; he seemed pleased with my thought about Plato having a sense of humour. 'We can only assume that he was human like the rest of us with his own peculiar quirks of behaviour,' he said. 'But, getting back to the question of whether natural pleasures are the same as necessary ones, I would say that, back in Plato's day, all food was natural and, therefore, necessary. The Mediterranean Sea was never too far away, so fish was part of their daily diet. There was also meat from goats and sheep. The warm climate was also favourable for growing grapes.'

'The picture is similar today,' I continued. 'On our farm we produce olive oil from olives and cheese from goat's milk. We also grow a lot of vegetables and there is an abundance of walnut trees. What we are describing is the Mediterranean diet which is regarded by many as the best diet in the world - it's all natural food.'

'So, can we conclude from our discussion that all

natural food is the same as necessary food?' he questioned.

'I'm not sure that we can,' I replied hesitantly. 'I've read in the dialogues that he was against eating spicy food even though it comes from a natural source.'

'Yes, that is so,' Aristocles mused. 'Plato lived in a different world. He thought that giving men anything other than plain food made them lazy and decadent so that they were unfit to protect their city from an invading army. He talks about the dangers of having too many Syracusan dinners with lots of spices and sweet sauces.'

'If that is the case, eating spicy food is natural but not necessary and, therefore, should not be eaten if someone wants to live their life in the mean.'

'Yes. It would seem that he would agree with you based on our discussion so far,' he said. 'However, it's possible that Plato would reconsider his views in the light of new knowledge coming forward. For example, if he was able to come back at a future time, I think he would argue that all food harvested from natural sources are necessary pleasures including ingredients that are used to make spicy dishes. What is unnecessary, he would say, is when people consume to excess.'

I looked at him quizzically wondering why he had chosen to come up with the ridiculous notion of Plato being alive today. There was something about his demeanour that made him come across as superior at times. 'He would get on well with Morris,' I thought, but I didn't know what to say in reply. After awhile, I said: 'So what you're saying is that all food and drink are necessary pleasures when they come from a natural source.'

'That is my conclusion,' he replied, with a nod of his

head.

The conversation suddenly dried up and so we drank our coffees and gazed around and beyond to the people walking along the sun-bathed street.

I broke the silence by saying: 'There's another problem today which we haven't talked about yet. Compared with Plato's time there are now hidden constituents in food and drink, some of which are not natural ingredients. For example, people may consume very little but, because the ingredients of a particular food or drink are artificially processed, they put on weight more so than if they had eaten the same quantity from a natural product!'

Aristocles looked astonished. 'Tell me more about this. How can food be artificially made?'

'I love coming to cafés like this one. It has a relaxing atmosphere and it gives me the opportunity to escape for awhile from my research. We have already concluded that the coffee is good within moderation but if you look at the other products for sale, you don't know, just by looking at them, how healthy they are and the proportion of the ingredients that is artificially processed. Look around at what people are eating and what is being displayed on the counter. There are lemon tarts, blueberry muffins, flapjacks, mini-cakes, etc, but if you decide to eat just one of them every time you come here, you will find you're putting on weight even though you haven't consumed a great deal. The same goes for the fizzy drinks on display.'

'I'm beginning to find myself lost for words,' he replied. 'As you know, I come from a remote village in Geece but I can't believe that things have changed so much ... Tell me more!'

'One moment,' I said, and quickly got up and walked to

the counter. I returned with a cellophane-wrapped chocolate brownie in my hand, which I opened up and offered a piece to Aristocles. He placed it in his mouth with some caution.

'What do you think?' I asked.

'It tastes nice, but too sweet for my liking,' he replied, wiping his sticky fingers on a paper serviette.

'You're probably not used to eating sweet things, that's why it tastes much sweeter compared with people who eat them on a regular basis. Let's look at the ingredients listed on the back of the wrapper.' I took my glasses off and stared at the small print. 'What it says is that it's mainly made of almonds and chocolate which seems natural enough. Almonds are almonds but the chocolate! ... It comes from the seed of the cacao tree but sugar is always added in production to make it sweet and more tempting to eat.'

'So, correct me if I'm wrong,' he replied. 'Are you saying that sugar is used as an additive to natural food to make people want to buy more of a particular product?'

'Yes ... It can be put into cakes, pies, bread, cereals, and even meat products just to make them more tasty and desirable. If you look at this chocolate brownie with a total weight of 60 grams, it reads that there are 33 grams of sugar in it, which is more than half the overall weight of the bar. This not only means that more and more people become over-weight from eating such products but also, in extreme cases, there is an increased risk of developing complications such as diabetes and heart disease.'

'There are so many questions to ask,' Aristocles uttered, shaking his head. 'But don't let me stop you in full flow. Go on with your analysis.'

'Apart from sugar, the brownie also has a large fat content listed here at 27 grams, A large proportion of this is processed fat which is the worse kind of fat because the body finds it difficult to burn it off through exercise. It says here there are also preservative chemicals added such as potassium sorbate, coded as E202, which increases the shelf life of the product. Another chemical is lecithin, E322, made from soya to give it extra flavour. It doesn't say on the wrapper but lecithin can be genetically modified. In other words, its chemical structure can be changed in a laboratory to make it more effective in enhancing flavour.'

'I can see now why you say there are foods and drinks that are artificially processed because of all the extra ingredients mixed in. These are far removed from what was conceived to be natural in Plato's time.'

'I can give you some more examples although we're running out of time,' I said, realising that we had been in the café for nearly two hours. 'Vanilla, for instance, is used to flavour cakes, biscuits and ice-cream. Not too long ago, the ingredient would come from vanilla pods but nowadays it is chemically constituted from sawdust and chemicals that are also used to make petrol.'

'You mean the same stuff as they put in cars?' Aristocles replied, putting on a contorted face.

'Yes! ... And there's more!' I flicked through my notebook. 'Here it is ... It says, sugar can be genetically modified in laboratories to create artificial caramels which are then used as dyes to colour soda drinks and muffins! ... Here's another one! ... Using margarine rather than butter is unadvisable. It is almost plastic in composition and shares twenty seven ingredients with paint!'

'What you've just described is like an explosion in my mind. There's so much for me to take in. I obviously know less about this modern world than I originally thought' He looked despairingly down at the froth still lingering at the bottom of his coffee cup.

'Never mind,' I replied, sensing his mood change. 'You can borrow one of my books on nutrition, if you want? I have so many of them in my flat and there's quite a lot of overlap in the material.' I took a book out of my bag and handed it to him. 'Here, you can borrow this one.'

'You're very kind,' he replied, gazing at the cover. He then looked up at me with his searching, blue eyes. 'I'll have to return it ... Do you want to meet up again?'

'Of course!' I replied automatically, not thinking too clearly as to whether meeting up again was a good idea. 'Perhaps you can help me with the following chapter ... That's if you want to?'

'I would consider it an honour,' he replied. 'We are fellow academics helping one another in our quest to gain new knowledge and, besides, it's what your Grandfather would have wanted!'

'Hopefully, I won't disappoint him!' I replied ambivalently.

'He would be very proud of you, I know that ... And, when we meet again, we can have more pleasurable experiences including drinking coffee?'

'As long as pleasures are not your master,' I replied flippantly.

'That goes without saying! But, what I find alarming is what you've told me about all the extra ingredients being added to food and drink so it becomes difficult to detect what is natural and what is artificial. That is worrying especially when people are likely to damage their health without them knowing!'

'It has become a wholesale practice in this modern age,' I replied. 'Some farmers even feed their cows and sheep on synthetic steroids so they become heavier, which means they make more money for every animal slaughtered. Most people seem to go along with the status quo, unthinkingly, and eat what is presented to them on the supermarket shelves.'

'It appears that the sophists have taken over the world!'

'It seems that way. Another term to express this type of exploitation is 'capitalism'.'

'It all sounds depressing,' he replied, shaking his head and giving out an audible sigh. 'People should be allowed to go back to growing and eating their own food. You've already pointed out that the Mediterranean diet is one of the best in the world.'

'That would be fine if people could find the space to grow their own fruit and vegetables, but much of the food comes from commercial farms that use chemical fertilisers and pesticides for greater crop yields. These chemicals eventually degrade the surrounding soil to the extent that more and more fertiliser is needed every year to ensure similar crop yields. There is much more I can tell you if we had more time. Did you know that there is a decline in the honey bee population as a result of this chemical explosion?'

'Enough! No more! I've got the message,' Aristocles replied, shaking his grey head. 'So much has happened since Plato's day. It all sounds like the world is going through a new dark age. Let's leave our discussion now and reflect on what we've said. I have people in my village that I can talk things over with, and there is much reading and thinking to do as well. Thanks for the loan of this book. I am sure it will be very useful and I should know much more the next time we meet.'

Aristocles helped me gather my notes together and then we made our way out of the café. We crossed the tramlines into Piccadilly Gardens and walked on until we reached Queen Victoria's statue. The sun was high in the sky.

'Well, I found the whole experience very interesting,' he said. 'Thank you, once again.'

'You're welcome. It has been really worthwhile and has given me the impetus to start writing again.'

'Good! I'm pleased ... What's your next chapter going to be on?'

'It's going to be about evaluating the claims made in the food and drinks industry. I intend to use Plato's philosophy on sophism as a template for analysis ... There are so many dubious claims out there.'

'A fascinating area of research ... I can't wait to meet up again.'

'How will I know when we need to meet up again?' I asked him.

'Don't worry. I have your email address. Just wait for a similar message coming through.'

Then, we parted with a smile. As I walk away, I instinctively turned to see him waving his rainbow stick. Then, he strode off, behind the large black statute.

A Surfeit of Sophists

I came away from Piccadilly Gardens in a kind of haze – like the feeling you get when you emerge out of the darkness of a cinema and the film stays with you as you walk down the street. Images of Aristocles flashed through my mind – he seemed to know so much about me!

I was too mixed-up to return to the university and so I walked down Mosley Street and up the steps into the Manchester Art Gallery. I decided to lunch there - choosing a goat's cheese and fennel tart from the menu. Afterwards, I browsed around the upper floor. I wandered randomly, not having a plan in mind, but I remember liking the bright colours of the Pre-Raphaelites and, in contrast, the large, mournful painting of the Greek poet, Sappho.

I was too distracted and restless to stay there long; there was so much for me to think about. I decided not to go back to the university that afternoon, so I walked down the grey-stoned steps and out into the bright sunshine, across the tramlines, and onto the platform at St. Peter's Square. My tram soon came along and I let it take me and my thoughts along the track to my flat near to the Media City.

There was so much to get my head round. 'Who is Aristocles really?' I asked myself. Definitely a man who knows a lot about early Greek philosophy, but he could have been an old, professional actor with his wand-like rainbow stick as a prop. None of it made any sense. I believed he was telling me the truth about Grandfather but I was unsure about the extent to which they were close friends. Surely, Grandpa would have told me something about him? If he had asked Aristocles to keep an eye on me, then why didn't he tell me of his intentions before he died? Then, there was my email address he passed on to him. Why didn't Grandpa tell me anything at all about any of this during the last few months of his life?

I was also annoyed with myself for not asking Aristocles any questions about where he was living and when was he planning to return to Greece. These thoughts churned around my head for the rest of the day and I couldn't settle on anything.

When I eventually got to my flat, I did something I rarely do. I brought in a Chinese take-away and then spent the evening mindlessly 'channel-surfing' whilst drinking half a bottle of Marbella wine. I went to bed at the usual time but couldn't get to sleep; it was gone midnight before I eventually drifted off. When I awoke, I realised it was too late to meet up with the early birders, so I went straight to the library. I made the decision not to tell them anything about Aristocles. It would have been too difficult for me to explain everything, and I wasn't sure I wanted to anyway.

Despite all my thoughts and unanswered questions about Aristocles, I soon settled back to a rhythm of work and made good progress in the coming weeks. I kept to my routine of going in early, meeting up with Morris and Christiana, and then settling down in my usual spot in the library. Throughout May, the sun shone and nature came out to welcome it with a blossoming of flowers and the sound of bird song. Morris got teased about his insistence that it rained on average three days out of five. He wouldn't be gainsaid and insisted that the good weather we were having was making up for the persistent rain we had in the winter months and, besides, it rains at night when we're all asleep!

During this period, I got to know Lisa better. I would seek her out after I'd been in the library for several hours, and we would go for a walk in Whitworth Park and then have a snack in the gallery restaurant. She looked just like an art student with her frizzed hair and dungarees, and people had no idea of her true predicament. As we sat in the glass-lit restaurant, she told me more about her home life, and how her father rose through the ranks to become the senior marketing executive for a well-known cereal manufacturer.

She told me how everything came to a head on the final day of her A level exams. She came home from school to find her mother wasn't there. In her bedroom, there was a note stating she had left home and would contact her as soon as she could. The reason for leaving wasn't given except for saying that her father had gone too far this time. It also said she was going to stay with an old school friend who lived in Chester, and would contact her as soon as she could.

When her father came home, he didn't seem at all surprised; and then, the following weekend, Maureen, and her daughter, Charlotte, moved in. Lisa soon realised they had been cheating on her mum for ages; Maureen worked in the same office. 'So much for his late night overtime!'

On the Monday morning, her father and Maureen went off to work together in his BMW as if nothing had happened, and Charlotte went off in Maureen's Mercedes to her hair stylist job in Wilmslow. While they were away, Lisa was expected to do the housework such as making the beds, cleaning, and getting the dinner ready for when they came home.

Bit by bit over this period, the rest of her story came out as we continued to meet up at the Whitworth Gallery Restaurant. Lisa explained that her father didn't want to talk about the reasons why her mum had left home. His standard reply was: 'It's her decision and there's nothing more to say!' Sometimes, in her imagination, she suspected foul play but she had her mother's letter as proof that she was alive and living somewhere in Chester - it was definitely her handwriting.

Every day, Lisa expected her mum to get in touch. She hadn't been allowed a mobile phone but she thought her mum would contact her via the house phone when everyone was at work or, failing that, by letter. After two months, she was in a state of mental and physical exhaustion being ground down by everyone's demands especially from Maureen and Charlotte who seemed to treat her as their personal servant.

She took a job in the local shop thinking that Maureen and Charlotte would be more sympathetic towards her, but they would have none of it! They expected the same level of housework regardless of her part-time hours; the whole situation drove her deeper into exhaustion and despair. There was still no message from her mother and so she decided to take up the offer from one of her friends to move in with her on a temporary basis whilst her parents were away in Marseilles. That was the point of no return; from then on, she lost all contact with her former life and eight weeks later she was living on the streets of Manchester where people were more generous with their handouts.

It wasn't surprising that Lisa became the main topic at our early bird coffee club. Christiana was really upset about Lisa losing touch with her mother. She thought that Maureen and her daughter acted like a pair of cuckoos and pushed her out of the family nest. 'It's absolutely disgraceful,' she exclaimed. She then made an announcement that it was going to be her quest to bring mum and daughter back together again - she would start by searching the local missing persons' websites.

Morris looked sceptical, but then announced there must be practical ways of helping Lisa such as finding her accommodation so that she could apply for jobs. He said he would talk to his father about her and also contact the social services.

By the end of May, I had finished my chapter on Plato's mean as well as filling another book of notes about Plato's views on sophistry ready for the next chapter. When I eventually saw Doctor Pendlebury, he was his usual non-committal self as he flicked through my work and suggested vaguely about various additional material that would possibly improve it. This time, however, as I was about to leave, he actually gave me a smile and said it was on the right lines and to keep the momentum up for finishing by December. 'Praise indeed!' I thought.

For the first time, I sensed I was making real progress with my thesis and my enthusiasm seemed to rub off on Lisa. We continued our chats at the Whitworth Gallery, and Christiana and Morris started to come along as well; together we would talk about our plans for getting her off the streets.

For awhile, we all remained in a bubble of expectancy, but one thing my life has taught me was not to assume that things will always work out for the best. As the summer equinox approached, I had a phone call from

Yanis saying that Mama seemed to be more breathless and Doctor Theo had decided to send her off for another scan. When I phoned her, she said she was feeling just fine and I wasn't to worry.

The following morning, I was literally brought down to earth. I was seated at the breakfast bar drinking coffee, when I heard the sound of toast popping out of the toaster. Getting up suddenly, my foot somehow got caught in the metal bar of the chair which twisted me around and propelled me across the room. My hands went out to break my fall but my elbow caught the corner of the TV stand as I fell. Almost immediately, the joint swelled up.

I was in two minds as to what to do. I could move the arm but it was painful. I had planned to have a full day at the university, but would the elbow get better by itself or was there a fracture of some sort? I decided to wait until I'd finished my breakfast which I accomplished both awkwardly and painfully. I soon realised that I could hardly move my elbow and the swelling seemed to have worsened. Cursing my luck, I decided to go to the Accident and Emergency at the local hospital which was situated not too far from my flat and, all being well, I could get to the university later on in the day.

I expected a long wait and so I took my laptop and notes with me. Surprisingly though, I didn't have to wait long. I was triaged after 20 minutes and, when the hour was up, I was being shown the x-ray of my elbow by a kindly doctor who informed me it was badly bruised but there were no breaks. The pain seemed to ease with the news and when I finally emerged into the sunshine with my arm in a sling, I felt much better.

I walked back and caught a tram. As I wended my way

towards the city, I couldn't stop thinking about Mama - I decided not to tell her about my fall. 'She has her own health to think about – she would only worry.' At Cornbrook Station, I heard a pinging sound coming from the mobile phone in my bag. I took it out and scanned the emails to find there was one from Aristocles. It read: 'I am in the city again. Would you like to meet up and chat over a cup of coffee? The same rendezvous?' I emailed back to confirm I would be there in fifteen minutes.

Now he had contacted me again, the same thoughts came flooding back as to who he really was, but I found myself feeling really excited about meeting him once more. My rational self couldn't explain why this was so? He was a nice enough person even though he hadn't told me the whole truth about himself; and, it was uncanny how he seemed to pop back into my life whenever I was in some kind of stress.

I got off the tram at Piccadilly Gardens and walked over to Queen Victoria's statue; there he was, standing there twiddling his rainbow stick as if no time had passed since we'd last met.

'There you are, Alecta,' he said, with his usual big, smiling face. 'It's good to see you again, but what have you done with your arm?'

'I did it this morning ... Not looking where I was going,' I explained vaguely. 'But it's alright. I've been to the hospital ... it's not broken, just bruised.'

'That's good ... so you can conclude that the outcome is looking better than you first thought,' he replied. 'I recommend that you have a nice cup of coffee ... Agreed?'

'Agreed,' I replied, and allowed myself to be escorted across the square and tramlines, and into the café.

I found myself responsible once more for the walking stick as Aristocles went to the counter to order the coffee. He returned with a tray holding two cappuccinos and, to my surprise, a pear. 'I thought you might need to re-build your strength after what you've gone through,' he said, in a fatherly tone.

'Thanks, very much,' I replied, and then added. 'A good healthy choice!'

'We need to make sure you remain in the mean by eating wisely!' he said, chirpily. 'But tell me, how did you get on with your last chapter on Plato's mean?'

'Very well!' I replied, as I stirred my coffee. 'My tutor thinks it's good but it needs some minor revisions.'

'What do you need to do?

'I need to say more on the role physical exercise plays in maintaining good bodily health. Last time we met, we spent most of our time discussing the importance of healthy eating and drinking, so there was too much emphasis on that in my writing.'

'It sounds as though you only have minor revisions,' he said reassuringly. 'But what precisely do you have to include?'

'Remember the diagram we drew? I need to discuss physical fitness in terms of the mean. My own view is that people who are keen about fitness and exercise become excessive about it.'

'In what way?' he enquired.

'For a start, there're plenty of electronic devices keeping track of weight and fitness - some of them are software applications for mobile phones and watches. People can become obsessed about whether they've run a certain distance on time or whether they've improved upon their previous target. The same goes for people who go to the gym. Some of them become obsessive about the number of press-ups they've done or how many kilometres they've clocked up on those electronic running machines.'

'I don't see any harm in what you've described as long as people are doing it for the right reasons,' Aristocles replied. 'If they're doing exercise because they believe it's good for their health and want to live within the mean, then why not take advantage of these new devices?'

'I'd go along with that as long as they don't become too fixated about their bodies. The people who annoy me the most are the body beautiful types - the men who strut around like peacocks displaying their rippling physiques and the women who behave as if they're some kind of sex goddess.'

Aristocles gave out a chuckle as he thought about what I had said. 'There is an old adage where I come from,' he declared. 'We say - 'nothing new under the stars'. Plato would agree with you that gymnasts often fashion their bodies for the sake of vanity. In ancient Greece, most of the physical training was for military purposes which meant there were political reasons for being strong and healthy. However, Plato was against programmes of violent exercise as he thought they not only brutalised people but also made them lazy.'

'This is relevant for my revisions,' I answered enthusiastically. 'It reminds me of what Plato said somewhere about a good soul improves the body rather than the good body improves the soul.'

'It's in the Republic. It's the nature of the soul that determines what's good for the body and not the other way round. What's special about Plato's philosophy is that he doesn't make any exceptions - what's right for one person is right for another. So, even in war, a warrior is expected to fight honourably with his soul fully engaged in what he's doing rather than giving way to savagery.'

'I've read about this. The Greeks were greatly influenced by Homer and his epic poems of the Iliad and the Odyssey,' I added.

'That's correct. There was an expectation amongst the would-be heroes to have a duty to themselves which affects the way they treat others. The correct behaviour on the battlefield was very important and was considered to be a form of excellence. The Greeks had a name for it – aretê. People were expected to be honourable in all circumstances, even in their normal lives. Plato would say that the soul, or if you like the mind, must be in control if people are going to stand a chance of leading a honourable life. There is no place for brutality in any shape or form.'

I nodded automatically as he spoke, but I was only half-listening to what he was saying. My elbow was aching and I was rubbing my hand over the joint. 'It pains you, doesn't it?' he said.

'It's starting to throb, which maybe a sign it's getting better.'

'Have one of these!' he insisted, opening up the top of his rainbow stick to reveal lots of green-looking pills. 'I call these my travel sickness tablets but my physician informs me they are equally good for pain relief of other sorts. I'll get a glass of water from the counter.'

A few minutes later, I was feeling much better and the pain in my elbow had subsided. 'Has it worked?' he asked.

'I believe it has!'

'They never fail to work. It's an old Greek remedy, made from natural ingredients - especially walnuts,' Aristocles replied, with just a hint of a smile.

For awhile, we sipped our coffees and talked about other things. We were both distracted by the beautiful weather and found ourselves talking about the warm Mediterranean climate that always makes Greece a very special place to live. As we chatted on, we both experienced a sudden yearning for our home country. We deeply missed it! He was amazed when I told him about all the changes in Athens - he said he hadn't been there for many, many years. I explained that the Acropolis was still there but, down in the streets, there were always lots of tourists, and cars pumping out noxious fumes.

He seemed saddened to hear about all this but soon brightens up when I told him about the Theatre of Dionysos. A sparkle returned to his eyes. He was soon reminiscing about the Sophocles' plays that were performed in its great arena. We were lost in the moment of memories whilst the coffee was slowly sipped dry.

'Would you like another cappuccino? ... It's my turn to get them,' I asked, once our thoughts came back to present time.

'Yes, I would. But you stay here and rest your arm. I'll get them.'

Aristocles got up and went to the counter. Whilst he was gone, I imagined myself strolling down Solonos Street and drinking coffee under the awning of my favourite café. I was still daydreaming when he returned with the cappuccinos. 'I'm beginning to get a fondness for coffee drinking,' he said, with a wink.

'It's not without its downside,' I remarked. 'The caffeine will keep you awake at night if you have too much of it.'

'We're back to the mean again ... Everything within moderation ... Desiring more is not the same as knowing what's good for us.'

'The moral of the story is that the mind must intervene to tell us to stop drinking!' I added. Aristocles nodded his head as he raised his cup to his lips.

'Do you remember that chocolate brownie we examined the last time we were here?' I asked.

'I do ... It was very sweet tasting and full of undesirables.'

'Well, I took the wrapper away with me and did some research on how long it would take for me to burn off the calories assuming I had eaten the whole bar.'

'I learnt about calories from that book you lent me,' exclaimed Aristocles, whilst wiping coffee froth from his moustache. 'I read that it's the energy produced when foods are burnt as fuel such as when you exercise. The problems occur when the calories eaten are not burnt off, which means they are stored as extra body fat.'

'You've certainly done your research.'

'I showed the book to my intellectual friends in the village ... They were most interested. They even tested me to see whether I understood the concepts so that I would be more prepared once I met up with you again ... But I've interrupted you - tell me more about your findings concerning the chocolate brownie.'

'There's an electronic reckoner on the web where you can put in your running speed and weight and it comes out with the amount of time you need to run to burn off the calories you've consumed. I calculated there were about 330 calories in that brownie which means that I would have needed to run for about one hour at a speed of 6 kilometres per hour to burn it all off. When you think that the government recommendation for women is 2,000 calories per day, I would only need to eat 6 chocolate brownies to reach my limit. Think about all the hours of running I would need to do to get rid of all those extra calories if I ate them on top of my regular diet!'

'You'd be spending most of your time running!' Aristocles exclaimed. ' ... But what about this pear? How many calories do you think there are in that?'

'I would say about 90 calories, which is just over a quarter of the calories of the chocolate brownie even though they are more or less the same weight. I would only have to run for something like 5 minutes to burn it off or just walk naturally at a steady pace for twenty minutes, which I would do anyway as I go about my daily life. What's more, eating the pear is much healthier for me.'

Aristocles listened intently then started to smile. 'As I was waiting for you at the statue, I was curious to know how many overweight people were passing through. My test was whether a passer-by would be able to run fast enough to avoid the horns of a charging bull, assuming that they could jump over an imaginary fence once they got to the tramlines. Out of 30 people, I reckoned that 12 wouldn't make it!'

'How strange!' I exclaimed spontaneously. 'I was doing something similar at the hospital whilst waiting for my arm to be seen to. There were ten people waiting ahead of me and I had time enough to assess their overall physical wellbeing. Four of them were very obese whilst another three were heading in the same direction. The vending machine was being regularly raided for high-priced, sugary snacks and drinks.'

'You would have thought those responsible for managing the hospital would ban unhealthy food and drink,' declared Aristocles.

'That would be the obvious thing to do!' I replied cynically. 'It's a way of making more money, together with the exorbitant hospital parking fees, to pay for the huge salaries of the senior management team.'

'Do you have any evidence to support that statement?'

'Call it intuition. There's no direct evidence but that's what I feel is happening.'

'So what you're saying, or feeling, is that senior managers are being dishonest in allowing sugary products to be sold on the premises?'

'Yes ... My cynical side would say that,' I answered, finding myself suddenly becoming angry at the thought of executives earning extra money by exploiting human weaknesses.

'You sound very passionate about the situation,' he replied, with a quizzical look on his face.

'Yes, I suppose I am,' I replied, and found myself thinking about Lisa's father and the way he'd personally prospered from selling sugary cereals. My mind then flashed back to the obese people I'd seen in the hospital. I could visualise them as they slowly raised themselves out of their chairs to waddle the short distance to see a nurse or the doctor. 'There is an obesity epidemic in this country and some people are exploiting it,' I finally said.

'Would you say there is a world-wide obesity problem?'

'Yes, I would, but not everywhere. There are areas in

the world where the people have to physically work hard on the land to provide for their families – they are usually very poor. In contrast, in the developed countries like this one, people have become less active and consume more food. There are some startling statistics about the health of our world. There is one which predicts that something like a fifth of the world's population will be obese by the year 2025.'

'That is staggering!'

'We must place a lot of the blame on the food industry. People don't realise that junk food and long periods of inactivity are literally killing them. In this country, the situation is fast becoming a national crisis with millions of people at risk of developing diabetes. It's not surprising that the cost to the nation's health service is growing out of all proportion.'

'What you're describing is a situation out of control.' Aristocles replied, with a shake of his head.

'The biggest problem today, as we discussed last time, is all those extra ingredients they put into food - especially sugar.'

'But why have world societies allowed this to happen? ... Aren't there any powerful people or groups trying to rectify the situation?'

'Dietary researchers are aware of the problems. Governments around the world are also aware but they're likely to be more concerned about the growing cost to the national debt rather than their citizens' health.'

'That would be your cynical side talking again?' murmured Aristocles.

I smiled at his obliqueness. 'Yes, I must admit - it is my cynical side coming through! However, I realise I need to hide my cynicism and be more objective when writing up.'

'Remind me again what you're writing about in this chapter?'

'I want to use Plato's philosophy as a way of assessing the knowledge claims made by the food and drinks industry. I need to make a strong case to show how sophists are still around today. These are the capitalists hiding within big corporations. They pretend to be on the side of the consumer but they're only interested in making more money for themselves. One of the ways they do this is by giving out misleading information when selling their products.'

'Plato thought that sophism was the enemy of philosophy,' Aristocles remarked. 'He despised sophists as haters of truth and corrupters of minds but, in terms of these modern-day sophists, you'll have to give me more information so I can understand what's going on.'

'There're plenty of them around especially in marketing. Children are particularly vulnerable. For example, if you take breakfast cereals, children are attracted to bright colours and jazzy words.'

'They're also attracted to those cheeky-looking animals on the packets,' he remarked. 'I've seen them in your supermarkets.'

'These marketing sophists will do anything to entice children to eat their sugary products. A bowl of cereal tastes nice because of the high concentration of sugar but it has limited nutritional value and they need to exercise to burn off the excess calories ... I've done some research.'

At this point, I flicked through the pages of my notebook. 'Here it is! ... I've found out that most of these cereals have between 10 and 11 grams of sugar for a 30 gram serving. This is high when you compare it with the World Health Organization's recommendation for good health of 25 grams per person per day.'

'From your figures, I would say that a typical child would soon reach their daily recommended limit. They're almost there with just their breakfast, and they have the rest of the day ahead of them for more sugary temptations.'

'Child obesity is a worldwide problem,' I continued. 'According to what I've read, forty million children under the age of five are considered to be overweight. As you say, there are plenty of extra temptations to push them above the 25 gram limit. Sugar-sweetened soda drinks is another danger because they are well-liked by children. Just one can of soda contains something like 40 grams of sugar, which means they've exceeded their recommended daily limit in one go!'

'It's similar to that chocolate brownie you were talking about.'

I nodded in agreement. 'I feel as though I'm going on a bit. But one of the problems today is that there are powerful and hidden forces at play and the vulnerable in society are often the ones who suffer.'

'You're not, as you say, going on a bit. You're just passionate about your area of research. It seems to be a world epidemic, but why do you say these forces are hidden?'

'They're hidden and often insidious,' I replied fervently. 'There are powerful people within organisations that make lots of money even though their actions are detrimental to the health of millions of people worldwide.'

'You're going to have to give me more examples so I can understand this line of reasoning.'

I nodded and took a sip of coffee. Once again, Lisa's father flashed into my mind and I knew I had to tell him everything that had happened and how her father's greed and selfishness had driven her out of the family home. He was silent and open-mouthed as I recounted Lisa's sad tale. The story poured out from deep within my psyche; a subconscious urge to recount everything, even the finer details about Lisa's mum, and the two cuckoos - Maureen and Charlotte. I finished off by telling him how we, the early birders, were determined to get her off the streets and back into society.

'That's a very distressing story,' he said quietly, once I had finally finished speaking. 'I'm pleased you told me about Lisa. It's a story I can relate to my friends once I get back to my village ... It also says a lot about you, Alecta.'

'She was in a desperate situation ... I had to do something!'

'But most people would have just walked by and done nothing. You're what they call a Good Samaritan, Alecta.'

'Lisa is one of the millions in the world who are pushed on to the scrap heap through no fault of their own, I had to help her! ... But, coming back to our discussion, I would say that Lisa's father, as a senior marketing executive, is one of those hidden and insidious people. He doesn't care about the children who eat his sugar-coated breakfast cereals. He has a mansion, a flashy car, and he makes lots of money in the process.'

'You make a strong case.'

'My argument is that the top management in large corporations, like Lisa's father, are aware of the vulnerability of children but exploit them anyway for their own monetary advantage. There is also another side to this. Nowadays, children have access to computers and, when they go online, there are plenty of clever adverts tempting them to buy their favourite things.'

'Are you talking about general things or specifically about health products?' questioned Aristocles.

'This applies to all products marketed for children but I want to emphasise what's going on with food and drink. Let me give you an example. It's now possible for children to watch online entertainment that have pop-up adverts specifically coaxing them to purchase sugary products. The programs are very sophisticated and much of the data is captured on databases so that, when the children go back online, these marketing organisations already have a vast amount of information about them in terms of their likes and dislikes, which means they can target them directly according to their preferences.'

'As you are aware, I come from a remote part of the world. Are you saying that these computers are so designed to coerce children into buying sugary snacks?'

'That's correct, except that it's the software that's doing all the harm in a very subtle and clever way. For example, children may be watching a video for educational reasons but the embedded images in the software can trigger a response to entice them to buy a particular product. These images may even be subliminal so they enter their minds subconsciously.'

'Do you mean that the children don't know they've seen these images but it's registered in their minds anyway?'

'That is exactly what happens. So, when they go to the shops they are more likely to buy the product that is stored as a subliminal image in their minds. Another example I can give concerns children and their mobile phones. There are ingenious programs which can keep track of what they're doing at any moment in time and can push advertisements at them according to their personal tastes and interests. It's a form of brain-washing and often they don't know what's happening to them. It's got to the stage where software can determine their location and suggest which nearby shops are available that stock their favourite confectionery. You feel you're being watched all the time!'

'As I've already said, I come from a remote part of Greece and don't often know what's going on in your world. But when I come back to this city, I understand something of what you're talking about. People are so besotted by their phones they hardly look up and seem to want to bump into one another. They're not aware of the beautiful architecture and the blue sky above their heads … They're in their own bubble-world!'

' … Their own electronic bubble-world!' I added. 'And whilst they're in it, these marketing sophists, who I've decided to call 'The Invisible Persuaders', are controlling people's lives!'

'I like that description – 'The Invisible Persuaders',' he replied, wagging his index finger at me. 'Now you've mentioned it, being invisible reminds me of a story that Plato recounted in one of his dialogues about a shepherd called Gyges who lived in Lydia.'

'Is it a Greek fable?'

'Not originally, because the story came from Lydia but it was popular in Athens in Plato's time … I'll give you a brief account of it so you can get an idea why it was popular. It goes like this: one day, there was a storm and an earthquake which opened up the earth near to where Gyges was tending the King's sheep. He descended into the fissure to find a naked figure, lying prone with a golden ring on one of the fingers. He took the ring and returned to the outside world. He soon discovered that it had magic powers; every time he turned the stone on the ring towards the inner side of his hand, he instantly became invisible. The story goes that he used this new found power to seduce the Queen of Lydia and together they conspired to kill the king and take over the kingdom.'

Aristocles took a sip of his coffee and waited for my response. 'I suppose the moral of the story is that if you think you can get away with something which is morally wrong, some people will do it!' I said.

'That's correct. It's a story about Plato's idea of justice. He says that the highest level of injustice is for people to pretend they're just and honourable when they're not.'

'So, if we use Gyges and his magic ring as a modern metaphor, these marketing executives have their own ring of invisibility. They are unseen and unknown outside their corporations and they instigate sophisticated software to persuade vulnerable people to purchase items without them knowing they're being persuaded and who's doing the persuading!'

'So it would seem,' Aristocles replied. 'At least the audience in ancient Athens knew who was making a speech and were able to question that person's honesty, and decide for themselves about the truthfulness of what they were saying!'

' ... and Socrates would have been there like the proverbial gadfly questioning and testing the veracity of what was being said,' I added.

'Indeed, he would! He would have been making sure the arguments put forward were based on reason, and not orators swaying the crowd because they'd been paid to do so.'

'The problem is that when you compare ancient Greece with today's society, there are many more people in the world.'

'I agree,' he replied, nodding his head. 'This world of yours is much more multifaceted than I ever imagined. I assume, these modern sophists have found it easy to use this complexity for their own advantage.'

'They have! I've identified another type of sophist that have taken full advantage of the situation,' I declared. 'They are just as powerful as 'The Hidden Persuaders' even though they are not hidden.'

'Tell me more!'

'Like all sophists, they're mainly interested in making money. They exploit individuals' weaknesses by brainwashing them into thinking they'll become healthier and happier if they follow a specific course of action.'

'Is this your cynical side coming out again? You're going to have to be more specific.'

'I'll give you some instances of what I'm talking about,' I replied, and started to thumb through my notebook until I found what I was looking for. 'There are lots of examples I can give, but here are some … There are numerous writers recommending specific dieting regimes. These can be of an extreme nature such as people who believe that eating mainly fruit is going to make them healthier, but the more likely outcome is that they'll eventually suffer from too much sugar in their blood and possibly contract diabetes. Then, there are those who swear that a palaeolithic diet is the best because our habits should mimic what our early ancestors would have consumed such as eating raw meat and drinking blood. Both of these I would class as extreme and can cause harm to people because they are not getting a good balanced diet. There are many more.'

'I'm not convinced that sophists are to blame, from what you've said so far,' he declared, scratching his white beard. 'People will always experiment.'

'It's all part of a mega-billion dollar industry and the marketing people tap into people's anxieties and stresses. They recruit so-called nutrition experts who push forward new diets and accompanying products with the pretence that they will make people slimmer and, therefore, happier. They want people to believe that what they are selling are miracle weight-loss solutions. The latest fad is eating protein shakes and so-called superfoods with added vitamins, all packaged in eye-catching tubs ... Why can't people just eat natural food harvested from Mother Earth without anything added?'

'I assume you are alluding to what they used to do in Plato's day,' Aristocles added assertively. 'I am prepared to go along with what you're saying but you must have other evidence to support your claim.'

He seemed to be in one of his dialectic moods, so I continued by saying: 'I recently went along to a bookstore not too far from here. I estimated there were over 300 separate books on dieting. There's lots of evidence there to show that these sophists are tapping into people's desires and fears!'

'I'm not sure I wholly agree with you. In the book you lent me, it states there's a strong case for being on a diet. Doctors, for instance, may recommend a specific diet for someone who has an eating disorder and needs a specific type of food. Diets are also a fundamental part of people's lives. They're chosen according to custom and where they are in the world. For example, Asian people eat a low fat diet of rice, vegetables, fresh fruit and fish. It also says that the Innuits - who I didn't know existed until I read about them - mostly eat fish, seal, and caribou. My point is that diets are good for you even though they depend on where you live in the world.'

'I agree with you ... but I'm not against diets as you've described them, it's dieting that is the main problem. The true diets are the ones that people adhere to throughout life, eating natural food regularly every day, whereas dieting is often a fad which people take up for a limited period in the hope of losing weight - they confuse weight loss with being healthy. Worldwide, there are hundreds of slimming clubs. They target vulnerable people to lose weight and, in the process, make money from selling their own dieting books and merchandise.'

'What do you mean by slimming clubs?'

I stared at him and wondered why he was still making out he was so ill-informed about the modern world. 'He's playing his old tricks again?' I thought to myself.

'I'm surprised you've never heard of them,' I replied sardonically. 'They are clubs that persuade people to meet up on a regular basis. Every week, the members weigh themselves to see how much they've lost. The idea is that the group encourages one another to shed the pounds by eating sensibly and doing more exercise.'

'I can't see much wrong with that idea. Plato was all for community support.'

'I agree. People do need extra encouragement to lose weight and I concede that it does work for some, but there are others who go on crash diets and lose weight for the wrong reasons. For example, people put on weight over a festive period and then wish to lose it, or they need to shed the pounds so they can display a youthful pose on the beach. It's referred to as being 'beach ready' and vanity is a big factor here. What seems to happen when the target weight loss has been reached is that dieting loses pace and people eat and drink unwisely again to celebrate the weight they've lost. When they return to work, they return to a stressful environment and so the rate of over-indulging increases. They end up with a weight problem again and so, there is an urge to reduce the calories once more. Yet again, good intentions go awry and the pounds creep back on.'

'You would think many of them would learn by their mistakes, as we've discussed already in relation to the mean,' he remarked.

'There's a statistic somewhere which states that 95% of diets fail, but I suspect that it's not just the diets at fault but the intentions of the people on those diets. Many of them have a false desire of wanting to be happier, but there's too much emphasis on weight loss for vanity reasons rather than eating healthily to sustain one's life as Plato would have us do.'

'You have put forward a compelling argument,' Aristocles replied. 'From what you've said, diets are a natural part of people's lives whereas dieting is associated with impulsive behaviour. Plato would say: it's not being infatuated with our bodies that brings about life benefits but wisdom, and that is the key to a contented life.'

'So, what are we going to call this new category of sophistry?' I asked. 'We've already identified 'The

Invisible Persuaders' now we need another name for this group ... How about 'The Body Deceivers'?'

'Let me think ... ,' he replied, gazing all around at the various shapes and sizes of the café-dwellers. 'Don't you think 'The Mind Deceivers' is a better term? After all, this type of sophist are deceiving people's minds about the way they see their bodies.'

'Yes, I agree. That is more apt,' I said, rubbing my elbow unconsciously.

'Would you like another one of my green pills. Is it still hurting?'

'I'm fine. It's more stiff than painful. But, the whole thing has made me feel very hungry. I think I'll eat this pear and I can exercise my elbow at the same time.'

'I suppose it's a shock to your system.'

'I'm alright, really,' I replied.

I ate my pear whilst Aristocles looked on. The conversation dried up as our coffee was sipped and the pear consumed. After awhile, he asked me about my home and family. I recounted memorable stories about my life on the farm with Mama, Yanis and Grandpa, and how we were very happy there. I went on to tell him about Grandpa reading Greek history to me in his study, and how he used his influence to gain a place for me on the philosophy course at Athens – although he always denied it.

The conversation shifted and I broached again how he had first met my Grandfather. Like the previous occasion, he became illusive, I would say even nervous, as if he was cautious about telling me the full story, or even the truth. He persisted with the original tale that they had met up, long ago, whilst studying for their undergraduate philosophy course and they became life-long friends. He was reluctant to tell me anything about their friendship in the years after their student days - as if he was trying to cover something up!

It wasn't long afterwards that he changed the subject completely by asking: 'Do you think we've identified all the different types of sophists for your research?'

'I'm not sure ... I thinks so,' I replied, wiping my hands on a paper serviette.

'It is a rhetorical question because I've found another type in this book of yours. There's a whole chapter about scientists using statistical analysis to distort their research results so that the conclusions concur with the hypothesis they want to prove in the first place. I've already thought of a good name for this type of sophist. I call them 'The Research Distorters'.

'It looks as if you've done your research ... I'm impressed!'

'Thank you, but I needed help from my academic friends back in my village to understand the concepts and terminology. I was never taught statistical analysis, and Plato would have been frowned upon it if had been in use in his day. The idea that pronouncements of facts could be based on probability would have been regarded as a sin against the gods!'

'Plato and his contemporaries were Pythagoreans, so they believed calculations were absolute,' I added.

'Do you know what BMI means?' he suddenly asked, changing the flow of the conversation.

'Yes. The Body Mass Index is used as a standard in health research,' I replied, wondering where all this was leading to.

'That's correct … I've read in your book that people are considered to be of normal weight when their BMI is between 18.5 and 25, overweight between 25 and 30, and obese for those over 30. What you find is that specific empirical research is expected to coincide with this accepted standard but, even when the results are askew, there are ways of using sophistry to make out their findings are more acceptable to the scientific community as well as a means of attracting more funds.'

'How can they attract more funds if the research is suspect?' I asked.

'They use 'weasel words' which is a term I've picked up recently,' he said, and then he proceeded to thumb through my book. 'Ah! … There are lots of examples here of research results being distorted … Here is one of them! It reads that there's a technique used to get the results that researchers want which is called 'statistical clumping' based on the grouping of research data. For example, if you want to compare people's eating behaviours using the categories of normal weight, overweight and obese, there is a problem with the last category because people who are marginally obese with a BMI of 31 are grouped together with people who are morbidly obese of 50 and above. This is bound to skew the results when compared with the narrower data bands associated with normal weight and overweight.'

'I see where you're coming from … I never thought about the problems of clumping until now!'

'It's all new to me as well!' he replied. 'But there's also another research paper that found that people who are overweight live the longest compared with the other two categories, but this was buried in the writing up as something they didn't want their readers to read!'

'How can they not mention an important finding like that if it was something that came out of the research?'

'They bury it! That's another term I've learnt recently,' he replied. 'They don't go as far as to remove the evidence as that would make them open to claims of dishonesty. Instead, they lose it in the main body of text.'

'It feels like they have their paymasters in mind when they do that,' I added.

'No doubt about it!'

'I see now why you call them 'The Research Distorters'. The art of statistics is used as a mask to warp the results!'

Aristocles nodded in agreement and had another sip of his cappuccino before continuing: 'The sophists of distant past wouldn't have been able to hide behind calculations of a dubious nature and there was always dialectic discussion as a safeguard against untruths. False claims to knowledge would have been found out through critical debate.'

'From what we've discussed, I would say that, in today's world, critical debate is difficult to guarantee. You would possibly need a mathematics degree to examine the claims made by these sophists.'

'There must be lots of good research which has been under-valued because of these distorting techniques,' Aristocles suggested.

I thought about what Aristocles had said. The idea of having 'Research Distorters' as a type of sophist in today's society would never have occurred to me; but he'd got me thinking. 'I remember reading about a person who was vilified by the scientific community even though his research was thorough and eventually proved to be correct.'

'Tell me more,' replied Aristocles excitedly.

'His name was John Yudkin, who was a British Professor researching in nutrition and health. He saw there was a correlation between heart disease and the consumption of sugar, and conducted a series of experiments on animals and humans to support his claims. In 1972, his book 'Pure, White and Deadly' was published with the main message that sugar is as toxic as smoking and alcohol, and should be consumed sparingly. His research concurred with the rise in post-war obesity rates as sugar became an ingredient in products such as fruit juices, soups, pizzas and bread.'

'You've forgotten about the chocolate brownies!' Aristocles added flippantly.

I smiled at him and continued: 'At the time, Yudkin was stigmatised by the scientific community as being completely wrong. The alternative camp put forward the claim that it was not sugar that was the main factor contributing to heart disease but saturated fat. It was this group of academics who were the most persuasive and were able to make their voices known to those who controlled the scientific purse strings. By marginalising and deriding Yudkin, these people built up a strong case for low-fat diets even though, as we know now, their claims were based on suspect research data.'

'There must have been powerful sophistry at work for his research to be rejected without any rational assessment?' Aristocles added.

'There was! Prestigious universities were involved with this cover-up as the herd instinct took hold and big money got in the way of doing genuine science. Large manufacturers of sugary drinks and foods ridiculed his work by putting forward research money for low-fat research and by instigating bad press to personally denounce him. It got to the stage where Yudkin was 'uninvited' to prestigious conferences and prominent journals refused to publish his research. In the end, he died an academic pariah almost forgotten by the research community.'

Why didn't he fight back?' he asked.

'He was too much a gentleman. The opposition played lots of dirty tricks to deride his research but he wasn't prepared to do the same. He carried on doing good research throughout his life whilst the opposition tried to rubbish what he did. Some of the international conferences were sponsored by the sugar industry which meant they only accepted papers that favoured the saturated fat hypothesis. For over 40 years, misleading advice was given to the public about the causes of heart disease and obesity, and governments around the world broadcasted inaccurate dietary guidelines on the back of it. Eventually, after he died, the good research came through to prove what he said was right all along. More and more researchers realised that high levels of sugar in the blood is controlled by the release of insulin from the pancreas but, when insulin cannot cope with the excess sugar, it is automatically absorbed into bodily tissue as fat. People inevitably gain weight!'

'I can't understand why it took so long for him to be vindicated,' Aristocles asked. 'From what you've said, his research was more valid than the low fat fraternity.'

'At the end of the day, people believe what they want to believe, and usually this means following the accepted advice at the time. We now know that taking saturated fats out of products and replacing them with sugar was a

40 year old fad which caused a lot of damage. People put on weight. More and more people around the world contracted Type 2 diabetes, and more people died from heart disease. Another outcome of this untruth was that certain food manufacturers made mega-profits. They took out the fat from slimming products and replaced it with sugar. People went along with thinking they were healthier when they were not.'

Aristocles sat quietly for awhile, deep in thought as he stirred his coffee. Eventually, he looked up and said: 'The picture you've presented is a world inhabited by unscrupulous people who will go to any lengths to make money. It's very sad ... I know that sophists are sophists no matter which age they come from, but I fear that these modern-day sophists are a lot more devious. They fit well with Plato's description of them - as paid hunters who peddle falsehoods and deceits.'

'Such is the world!' I sighed.

'Such have the sophists made the world,' Aristocles proclaimed, in a sombre tone. 'There have always been untrustworthy people but, in today's world, it seems there is now a surfeit of sophists increasingly causing havoc with people's lives.'

I nodded my head in agreement before continuing: 'There's another side to all this. I've read recently that many people don't want to open up a Socratic dialogue as they did in Plato's day. Instead, they go along unthinkingly with general opinion. Where there is debate, it has become a weakened replica – a place for scoring points over rival positions rather than listening and responding in a rational way. These types are more likely to go along with mob thinking or, if you like, mob-oratory'

'Mob-oratory is something that Plato would be familiar

with,' Aristocles remarked.

'The latest buzzword is 'post truth' which suggests that everything can be distorted to suit someone's pre-arranged position regardless of any rationale to the contrary.'

'Post truth must be a euphemism for telling a lie!' he added.

'Of course! For those who don't like the idea of having an honest debate, the phrase 'post truth' sounds authentic; something that craves respectability and enables someone to shift the blame back to their opponents ... It's very gladiatorial!'

'What a strange world you live in!' he replied.

The conversation suddenly dried up. Aristocles' attention was drawn to the coffee drinkers on the surrounding tables whilst I gazed out of the window at the city folk drifting by in the sunshine. 'I must make tracks soon,' I said quietly.

He turned his head towards me and gave me one of his big smiles. 'Do you think our getting together again has helped?'

'Yes ... It's been very useful,' I said. 'We've come up with some good names for our sophists: The Invisible Persuaders who use Gyges' magic ring; The Mind Deceivers who prey on people's desires and fears; and finally - The Research Distorters.'

'You have a good haul of sophists there!'

'But, it seems like we are accepting these modern sophists being in the world without doing anything about them! Is there anything we can do to safeguard ourselves from them or, at the very least, to mitigate their adverse effects?'

Aristocles screwed up his grey eyebrows as he thought. 'It follows from our discussion that the world is desperately in need of a new genre of Plato's guardians who are educated to use their talents for the benefit of society. We must ensure their university course reflects the demands and problems of today. For example, guardians in a modern setting must have the intelligence to interpret statistical data so they can question the validity of research. We need to eradicate the Research Distorters who hide behind false statistics and warp reality.'

'I agree with you. A good understanding of statistics is essential. We don't need another Yudkin scenario leading to another forty years in the wilderness!'

'Most certainly, we don't want that!' he replied.

In Plato's Theatetus, he gives a good explanation of what counts as knowledge and how it differs from mere opinion. At the end of the dialogue, he concludes that knowledge is having a true belief that something is true but a person must put forward a good account as to why that is the case. Therefore, our guardians must have the capability of scrutinising any claims put forward by these researchers.'

'I agree ... Also, these modern guardians need to be adept at understanding technology so that they can examine the ways in which sophisticated software entices people to buy products they don't really want.'

'They also need to be psychologists so they can comprehend what's going on in people's minds,' I added.

' ... And, they must be good communicators so that they can present their case to the public and be capable of winning the political debate whenever they're under attack. They need to guard themselves against the negativity of what you've identified as post truth.'

'A new style of university course is definitely required,' I replied, with some momentary excitement, but I followed up by saying: 'My cynical side chafes at me though. There's no guarantee that the public would take any notice of these guardians once they had finished their education, despite them having the know-how to uncloak these sophists.'

Aristocles screwed up his eyebrows as he thought about what I had just said. 'But we can turn to Plato again here!' he replied enthusiastically. 'Even in ancient Athens, he was aware that citizens would not be convinced by rational argument and so he recommended that some kind of story could be told so that the populace could be persuaded to support ideas for the good of society.'

'What you've just said seems like you're promoting Plato's noble lie?'

'Plato's has been much maligned by the idea of the noble lie. His intentions were honourable; he used it so that citizens could comprehend the importance of his philosophical ideas as a story which they would instinctively comprehend to be true. The same goes here. Some of the things we've been discussing can only be understood by statisticians and the like, and so the information needs to be relayed in a simpler form without the overall message being lost.'

'I see what you're getting at,' I replied. 'Not everyone understands statistical probability and you've already explained how results can be deliberately misrepresented, so what we need are stories that make people more aware of what's happening in society.'

'That's a good summary!' he said, enthusiastically. 'You've already mentioned in the Theaetetus that knowledge must be backed up by a good account. The same goes for any verbal description of something that is purported to be true. I believe there is such a thing as 'true stories' ... Can you think of any examples?'

'I have an excellent story in my notes!' I answered, as I flicked through newspaper articles in my scrapbook. 'This one explains what happened on the island of Guam after the Second World War. The Bikini Atoll in the Pacific Ocean was used for a series of nuclear tests by the United States, and there was substantial radioactive fallout on the island as a consequence. Prior to this, the islanders lived off native plants, fish and the produce of subsistence farming, but the nuclear tests changed all that. The radiation levels were too high for them to continue with their traditional ways and so they became dependent upon American imports of processed food. The islanders were also influenced by American culture and soon became hooked on fast food such as super-sized fries and sugary soda drinks, and they also became less physically active as time went on. It says here that, as a consequence of all this, over 55% of the population is now either overweight or obese. Diabetes is also high and so is the death rate.'

'That's exactly the account which should be put forward by would-be guardians to explain what can happen. Most people can relate such stories to the dangers of poor eating styles and lack of exercise which should counteract the bad rhetoric coming from the sophists. I also read about the Australian aborigines in that book of yours. They didn't fair well from western diet and many of them are suffering the same fate as the islanders on Guam with high rates of diabetes and lower life expectancy.'

'There're lots of similar stories even at a local level,' I replied, whilst looking at my watch. 'I'm going to have to go ... Thanks so much for all your help.'

'It's my pleasure. I'm pleased our meetings have been useful ... I've learnt a lot as well and I've much to tell my friends.'

I gathered up my notes and together we walked out on to Market Street where the sun was still shining brightly. Like the previous time, Aristocles accompanied me across the tramlines and the square.

'Well ... Thank you again,' I said, once we got to the statute.

'It's my pleasure ... What are you working on next?'

'Plato on goodness and wellbeing ... but I need to see my tutor about this because I'm not sure of the direction I need to take.'

'That's a very important topic; it's the foundation of all Plato's philosophy ... Would you like to meet up again?'

'If it's alright with you. Yes!' I replied.

'Well, look for my message then.'

'I will. Hopefully, it'll be my last chapter.'

With a smile, we left one another. As I walked away, I turned to wave but he was no longer there. In the corner of her eye, I saw his rainbow stick disappearing from view behind Queen Victoria's statue.

Goodness and Wellbeing

I worked hard on my sophistry chapter in the weeks after I last saw Aristocles and was able to present it to Doctor Pendlebury by early July.

Unlike some of my early chapters, this one came together rapidly; my thoughts flowed and words spilled out onto the electronic page. I felt it was well written but I wasn't sure what Doctor Pendlebury would think of it. When I finally met up with him several days later, he didn't give anything away apart from the occasional nod of his head as he read it through. By the time he had finished, the paper clip remained un-broken in his hand, which I thought was a good sign.

Overall, he said what I had written was 'sound' and he liked the way I had categorised modern-day sophistry, but he thought I had possibly stretched my reasoning too far by using Plato's 'noble lie' as a means of telling stories to illustrate the harm sophists are doing to people. I argued that the concept of a 'noble lie' really meant for Plato to be a 'noble truth' by giving people a better way of understanding complex situations in story form without them getting bogged down with multi-layered analysis. He accepted my position but thought I needed to provide a better rationale in the final thesis.

We went on to discuss my next chapter; he thought it would serve as a way of summarising my early chapters but the emphasis should be on how the individual could benefit psychologically from Plato's philosophy. He said I needed to re-introduce the notion of the mean within the context of happiness and wellbeing. He asked the question whether happiness is something invented by marketing people as depicted by their seductive adverts promising a better life, or is it rooted in an individual's search for goodness?

I came away from his office with that thought spinning around my head and with the inspiration to push ahead with my thesis. I also felt I was beginning to understand Doctor Pendlebury that much better – he still came across as being in his own, private world but, at the same time, there was something ploddingly effective about his tutoring style.

Throughout July, the morning sun would continue to trace my journeys into Manchester; I would have coffee, as usual, with Morris and Christiana, before taking myself off to my usual place in the library. During this period, I worked steadily on the next chapter and my new notebook began to fill up with thoughts and references.

Looking back, I would say I was becoming single-minded by the thought of finishing and returning to Greece no later than December. I kept up my contact with Lisa but found I was seeing less of her, although, by now, Morris and Christiana were regularly taking her to the restaurant at the Whitworth Gallery. They had become firm friends and committed to helping her in any way they could. Christiana had set up a website for her and, every day, spent time searching the internet for missing persons. Morris, on the other hand, was more secretive and said he was looking for practical solutions to get her off the streets.

During this period, I phoned home every week and Yanis would email me regularly with reports about Mama. She seemed to be fairly well if not a little breathless at time; she continued to take a siesta in the afternoon and was in good spirits. However, there was nothing to prepare me for the bombshell that came at the beginning of August. Yanis phoned to say he had found Mama collapsed in her chair and was now in hospital. Doctor Theo phoned later the same day to tell me she had regained consciousness, but they were all waiting for the results of a CT scan so that they could re-assess her condition.

I decided there and then, I would return home. I booked a flight and arrived in Athens two days later. When I arrived at the farm, I was surprised to find Mama back in her own bed, propped up with pillows - but she looked pallid and tired. She held her arms wide-open and we embraced; she was pleased to see me but said I shouldn't have come - my studies were more important. I assured her that wasn't the case; the main thing was I needed to be with her to make her well again. She seemed to accept what I'd said and gave me another hug as a kind of confirmation. That afternoon, I went to see Doctor Theo who informed me that the cancer was at an advanced stage and had spread to her liver and spleen - it was only a question of time. I enquired about her medication; she was taking morphine, which would have to be increased as the pain became more severe.

After a week, she said she was feeling better, so she decided to get dressed and move gently around. She continued to do small household jobs but was spending more and more time in her chair and, in the afternoons, took herself to bed. In the evenings, though, she seemed more of her usual self and would join us for dinner and then we'd stay up late reminiscing about times past.

During this period, the priest was a regular visitor and there were plenty of other callers. The local people were full of concern and some were just inquisitive, but friends came from far and wide and Mama was happy catching up with the news of other people's lives. All were made welcome and I had to make sure there was a plentiful supply of biscuits and coffee, and wine for those who needed it. August came and went, and her condition didn't seem to be getting worse but, by September, she began to remain in bed longer, becoming weaker by the day until she hardly had the strength to get up to go to the bathroom. At this stage, Doctor Theo was visiting every day with a regular supply of morphine. 'It won't be long now,' he would say, but Mama seemed to have different thoughts; she seemed to reach into herself and find new strength.

She died on the 27th October and the funeral took place a week later in the Greek Orthodox Church. I suffered greatly from the inevitability of it all, even though I knew it was coming. Yanis seemed to take it all in his stride and didn't show much emotion – a man thing, I suppose. He busied himself by arranging the funeral and sorting out the paperwork, whilst I wander around the farm or went on long walks like a lost goat. I couldn't surface from the deep depression I was in, and even the sympathetic emails and letters I received from Morris and Christiana didn't make me feel any better.

Yanis was aware of my depressed state and insisted I go back to Manchester and finish my thesis. He would manage everything at the farm and the sooner I finished, the quicker I could return. This was the second time in one year he had taken control of my life - saving me again from plummeting downwards into deeper despair. I felt a great weight had been lifted. What would I have done without my brother's love?

In early November, I flew into Manchester Airport;

there to greet me were Morris, Christiana and Lisa. We gave ourselves a group hug followed by a rapid fire of catch-up news. In the taxi we shared, I realised how much I had been out of the loop over the past three months; Lisa informed me that, thanks to Morris, she now had a social worker and was in hostel accommodation for two days every week.

The following morning, we met up for coffee at the Whitworth Gallery and continued our conversations from the day before. I asked Lisa if she'd heard anything about her mum - she shook her head. But Christiana declared it was only a question of time; we would eventually find her - safe and sound. Lisa smiled and thanked her for being so optimistic. It was then I realised how similar in temperament Christiana was to my own mother; they would have got on well together.

Morris was unnaturally quiet apart from chipping in now and again to correct us on various points as we discussed the woes of the National Health Service. Unexpectedly, as we were finishing our coffees and about to leave, he sprung something that stopped us in our tracks. He said he had been back to Lisa's house in Wilmslow disguised as a plain-clothed policeman with fake ID. It was Maureen who answered the door and he introduced himself as Sergeant Manning. He proceeded to give her an account of how his division was trying to trace the whereabouts of both Lisa Dawes and her mother, Lesley. At that moment in time, he said, they couldn't rule out the possibility of foul play.

He recounted how Maureen blushed as she was asked whether she knew anything about the whereabouts of either of them. She replied that she didn't know anything except for the fact that Lesley had left home in June, the previous year, and Lisa had left three months later, and neither of them had left any forwarding address. Morris gave her a business card with his mobile number and email address on and asked her to contact him if she had any information that could shed light on their disappearance. Before he left, he emphasised that he and his fellow officers were pursuing a definite line of inquiry and would be in touch.

We were all amazed at the audacity of carrying out such trickery. Morris had hidden talents that were unleashed now and then onto an unsuspecting world! Lisa wanted to know more, but Morris assured her there was nothing else to tell as the encounter had only happened a few days ago. We congratulated him on his subterfuge and left the Whitworth Gallery in high spirits.

The following afternoon, I met up with Doctor Pendlebury who was very understanding about my mother dying, and said there was no pressure on me finishing by December – there were extenuating circumstances and the appropriate paperwork had already gone through to the examinations board. Nevertheless, I told him I was determined to finish by the end of the year.

Soon afterwards, I was back in my usual place on the second floor of the library reading what I had already written about goodness and wellbeing. Despite my eagerness to finish and return to Greece, I found it difficult to concentrate, and repeated dark thoughts of not being able to see my mother again, halted my progress. I felt as though I needed to see her one more time and tell her how much I was missing her.'

An image of Aristocles came into my mind and I heard him saying: 'I understand what you're going through. Try not to worry - all will be well'. The 'ping' from my laptop was a welcome distraction and I wasn't surprised to find the email was from Aristocles, himself, wanting to meet up again. It was uncanny how he seemed to read my thoughts and sense that I needed to see him again.

The trees were now stripped bare of their leaves and a cold wind pushed against me as I made my way to Piccadilly Gardens. We met at the statue but it was too windy for us to speak, and so, we waited until we were seated in the café and drinking our cappuccinos. Outside, the yellow and brown leaves raced empty drink cartons down a sombre-looking Market Street. Five months had gone by since we were here last.

'I'm sorry to hear about your mother,' he said, reaching forward and holding my hand. 'I sensed there was something wrong and I hesitated about meeting again until now.'

'Thank you,' I replied, wondering how he always seemed to know what was going on in my life. 'There was nothing any of us could do. I knew she was dying of cancer, but even when you're prepared for what's to come, it's still a big shock when it happens. There's a cold finality about it - like an iron door slamming shut!'

'I know how you feel ... I'm an old man who has experienced similar heartache in my life.'

'I had to abandon my studies and go back to Greece. Grief is very debilitating.'

'But you're strong and, in time, you will come through this even stronger,' he replied, squeezing my hand.

I pulled away and stirred my coffee. 'I'm glad I was there for her in those final days. She reminisced a lot about her youth and how she fell in love with my father. I believe she found meaning to her life in those days before the end.'

Aristocles nodded in reply. 'I'm glad she found her peace ... Was she a religious person?'

'She was a Greek Orthodox but I would say she was more of a spiritual person than a religious one. Until she became really ill, she would regularly go to church but she would tell me she wasn't interested in the liturgy. She was there to commune with her God and, whether he listened to her or not, the main thing was that it always made her feel better and was able to face all that life threw at her.'

'That must have been a great comfort to her.'

I nodded, and sipped my coffee. 'But, there's so much to be done. Yanis is at the farm sorting out paperwork whilst looking after the goats and harvesting the olives. I feel guilty about coming back here. Perhaps, I shouldn't have returned.'

'I'm sure your brother will take care of things. Everything must seem up in the air at the moment and all your emotions are raw.'

I nodded, then he asked: 'What do you intend to do now?'

'I must return to Greece but, first of all, I need to finish my thesis - Yanis insists I should.'

'Do you have much more to finish?'

'Not, really. In the months after we last met but before I went back to care for my mother, I worked really hard ... Looking back, I think my subconscious mind must have sensed something was wrong but, for some reason, I couldn't stop working! And now, I just need to revise my current chapter and write the conclusion; I also need to go through the whole thesis to edit what I have already written. My English is good but I think and write like a Greek person. I use too many adjectives!'

Aristocles smiled and asked: 'So what do you need to do in your current chapter?'

'I need to look at what Plato says about mental wellbeing and goodness, and then summarise the whole thesis in relation to that.'

'Then, you'll need to relate wellbeing to Plato's notion of the mean.' Aristocles commented, stirring the froth on his cappuccino. 'It's all to do with things balancing for the sake of the whole otherwise there is disintegration and chaos, and that includes our mental lives as well.'

'Yes, it's all to do with searching for the 'greatest good' and creating a space in our lives for wisdom to grow.' I replied, but the words that came out sounded hollow and unreal. I lowered my eyes and started to finger my paper serviette. 'Not much of this has made a lot of sense recently,' I muttered.

Aristocles grey whiskery eyebrows twitched. 'Why do you say that?' he asked.

'During the past few weeks, I've had feelings of despair. At times, the world seemed to collapse in on me and any feelings of hope or happiness seemed to have been stolen away. When I felt this way in the past, it was always my rational self that came to my rescue ... but not this time.'

'What you've described doesn't surprise me, Alecta' replied Aristocles, changing his tense expression to a reassuring smile. 'You cannot be expected to behave like Socrates discussing philosophical points with your friends under a Mediterranean sun. You needed to do what was best for your mother, and that meant demonstrating your philosophy in a practical way ... Just because you're feeling low doesn't mean you're forsaking any of your beliefs.'

I gave out a sigh and could feel my eyes watering up. 'I do miss her,' I mumbled. 'Those last few days took their toll on me. I couldn't sleep, eat or even think straight. I just wanted to be there and make her last few days meaningful.'

'She knew that you loved her?'

'Yes, she knew that. We spent hours just talking about things especially the time when I was a child - memories of blue skies, lapping waves on rocky beaches, and picnics under olive trees. There were lots of old photos to go through. Yanis would come in and join us and we would talk long into the night. There were times when we couldn't stop laughing. The neighbours must have thought we were crazy!'

'They must have known what was going on.'

'Yes, they did ... And then, before long, she was gone!' I said, stirring my coffee distractedly. 'In those days after she'd died, I was full of emotions. The funeral was so bitter sweet. Hundreds of people came from Rafina and Athens and lovely things were said about her - wonderful things! There were times when I couldn't stop crying and then, I found myself laughing at the stories told about her life ... Everyone was so kind.'

Aristocles nodded and smiled. 'Plato writes that bereavement brings about both pleasure and pain - people smile through their tears. It is hard to make sense of it all when your feelings are so raw, but you must keep all those treasured memories close to your heart.'

I bit my lips and tried hard to stop the tears. 'The problem is - there are times when I can't visualise her. She seems to have drifted away from me now.'

'You will find her again, Alecta. There's no doubt about that,' Aristocles said, with one of his big smiles. 'Bereavement is a part of life's journey and all of us have much to learn from death. It is not necessarily the end of the journey.'

I glanced up at him as I wrestled with my emotions. 'At this moment in time, it seems like it is the end,' I replied.

'What I have to say to you now may not give you much comfort and I am not sure that it is appropriate at this moment, but I will say it anyway. Plato writes that the search for knowledge requires us not to be afraid of death. In fact, he says we should desire it! On the surface, this seems like a morbid fixation but, on the positive side, it is that which drives us on to make the most of our lives. We have already said that life is a moral journey but it is death that puts things into perspective - it adds purpose to our lives. It is an acknowledgement of our own mortality that shapes what we become.'

I shook my head and said: 'The dead can look after themselves, but they seem to have the ability to come back and haunt our minds.'

'We cannot let the dead interfere with our lives otherwise we become shackled to them,' he replied. 'What we need to do is to make sure they shine like a beacon to illuminate the path we need to take. I think that was the main message Plato was getting at when he related death to self-knowledge. Although, as you know, he did believe in an afterlife.'

'I don't know whether I believe in an afterlife or anything else at the moment.'

'That's fine. Beliefs don't always have to be expressed through words. Actions are also expressions of belief. You chose to delay your studies indefinitely to care for your dying mother. That says a great deal about you, more than words could ever express. You shelved your own ambitions at the time so that you could care for the person you love. This was more than instinct. She was the mother who brought you into the world and gave you her love as she raised you from a child. It says a lot about what Plato identifies as goodness. I am not saying that words are not important but we must judge people by their actions too; and so, what I am trying to say to you, Alecta, is that your kindness in looking after your mother was also an act of goodness.'

I looked at him in silence trying hard not to cry. 'Thank you! What you've said means a great deal to me - thank you for those kind words.'

'It's also a way of relating your actions to Plato's philosophy,' he replied. 'People may try to find goodness in their lives but don't know *how* to find it.'

I stared silently at this man who seemed to know more than he revealed. I thought about what he had said and, from deep within my inner being, feelings of calmness blew away the dark shadows of my thoughts. After awhile, I said: 'If you're bringing in philosophy here, I would say that there is a downside in trying to be moral.'

'What might that be?' Aristocles said, sipping his cappuccino.

Before I could reply, a gust of wind suddenly hit the front of the café; I heard the rattle of empty cartons racing down the street. 'Acts of goodness do not guarantee happiness,' I whispered.

'Yes, you're right in one respect. We try to be happy

but things come along to bring us heartache and pain. I think with Plato's philosophy, there is no guarantee of happiness because it's impossible to be in a permanent state of bliss, but a person can be content with their life even though they may experience pain. At the very least, I would say that Plato would advise us to avoid unhappiness by searching for the good in life.'

'Searching for the good in life can be problematical when you experience mental anguish,' I replied, thinking back over the last few months. 'There are experiences that make you feel terrible, and people do not seem to understand the sacrifices you make.'

'I would like to think that the 'feeling terrible' bit is short lived,' Aristocles replied. 'Finding the good can only be achieved through moral effort and you can find it regardless of other people being aware of your motives. You do things because you need to and not to please others. But let's come back to the idea of the good later on and continue our discussion by looking at the not-so-good in people's lives.'

I nodded and allowed Aristocles to continue with his train of thought. 'We've already discussed the dangers when we persistently over-indulge - remember our conversation about 'Tyrannical Man'? But Plato would argue that if we are conscious of our weaknesses we can direct our minds to doing something about them.'

'In a moral sense?' I asked.

He nodded, and then said: 'Doing something about our weaknesses requires us to respond morally and, hopefully, in so doing, happiness can come along because we are more positive about our lives. Plato also talks about the joys of experiencing true pleasures that are untainted by pain. These pleasures are associated with being aware of beauty in the world and being in awe of wonderful things.'

'So, what you're saying is that we cannot avoid pain in our lives but we can transcend pain by being conscious of the wonders around us,' I replied. 'But it is difficult to feel that way when we are experiencing pain.'

'That may be so, but Plato would argue that it is possible to transcend pain by finding a virtuous path in life. What we must always bear in mind with Plato's philosophy is that it is up to us to make choices for ourselves. The potential reward is to find contentment despite all that life throws at you. The main problems arise when we do our own throwing!'

'What do you mean by that?' I asked, giving a puzzled look.

'We can bring about our own pains through the bad choices we make. For example, when we think back to the diagram of the mean, there are lots of examples we discussed that can instigate our own downfall. We can over-indulge on drugs, food and drink, and we can under-indulge as well. But the list doesn't end there. Plato would also include other human weaknesses such as having too much pride, being overly jealous, or having excessive rage. His student, Aristotle, continued the debate after Plato, by stating that the soul is divided against itself and is pulled in many directions; and so, we must strive to live our lives in what Aristotle called 'the golden mean'.'

'Yes, I'm aware of the concept - virtue is synonymous with 'the golden mean' with two contrasting vices at the opposite ends of the extreme. So, for example, excessive rage and timidity are the two vices of the virtue of courage.'

' ... And shamelessness and bashfulness are the two vices of the virtue modesty - and so forth,' Aristocles replied. 'Both for Plato and Aristotle, virtue is considered to be the natural state of the soul and extreme behaviour causes it be harmed, sometimes irretrievably so.'

'Are we talking about the soul here as being something that survives after death?'

'It's up to you to decide. We talked about this before ... Plato believed that the soul was there before birth and survives after death, but in some of his dialogues he doesn't explicitly make that assumption and writes as if the soul is synonymous with the mind. The implication of what we're talking about is the same regardless of whether people believe in an afterlife or not. Plato makes it clear that the soul (or if you like - the mind) is either in control of our basic impulses or, alternatively, it becomes enslaved by the vices we have just been talking about. Our minds determine who we are!'

'So, how does all this relate to mental health?' I asked, thinking more specifically about my research.

'It's all in here!' Aristocles declared enigmatically, as he placed my book on the table and prodded it with his index finger. 'But, don't let's talk further until we've had another cappuccino. I need a warming cup of coffee in this bad weather!'

I nodded in agreement and, once more, was asked to look after the rainbow stick whilst Aristocles went to the counter. A few minutes later, we were sipping our cappuccinos again.

'This is very good coffee,' he said, wiping his whiskers with the back of his hand. 'I've discovered the wonder of the modern world – hot, percolated, frothy coffee!'

'You can't have travelled very far!' I replied jokingly, giving him a wink.

'I travel further than you think!' he replied, reciprocating my wink. 'But coming back to your question, I've found a very interesting section about mental health in this book of yours.' He put down his cup and started to flick through the pages. 'Ah!, here it is in Chapter 9 ... It says that several modern philosophers regard the concept of mental health as being invented by Plato! Can you imagine it! I couldn't believe it when I first read it. What a great tribute to him!'

I turned the book around and read through the appropriate section. 'This is good for my research! It gives several references relating to Plato's dialogues. It's remarkable when you consider most people think mental health can only be understood in a modern setting from Freud to the present day.'

'Many of the old ideas are the best,' Aristocles replied, trying hard not to sound too pleased with himself.

'There's a good reference here from the Timaeus,' I said enthusiastically. 'It says that just as the body becomes diseased so does the soul. It also confirms what Plato wrote about man's irrational desire to experience excessive pains and pleasures. In severe cases, this brings about madness to the extent that people go beyond the capability of helping themselves.'

'All good material for your chapter,' suggested Aristocles.

'The author also refers to Plato's Philebus by stating that to 'know not thyself' is the opposite to that which is written on the inscription at Delphi - 'know thyself'. The inference being that 'not knowing yourself' leads to delusion which eventually leads to a deterioration of the fabric of mental life.'

'This all fits in with what we've been talking about,' Aristocles replied excitedly. 'Excessive pains and pleasures can bring about delusion and madness - corrupting the natural state of the soul.'

I nodded and re-read some of the text. 'What this is saying is that health relates to virtue. We can improve the state of our mental wellbeing by acting morally, and this implies learning to pull away from unhealthy desires which Plato and Aristotle would identify as being tantamount to vice. Our good choices draw us closer to the natural state of our psyche.'

' ... Which is associated with Plato's mean. But, unfortunately, as we've discussed before, there are some people who can't return to the natural state of their psyche,' he said, as he sipped his coffee.

'It seems that you're right,' I replied, re-reading some of the text. 'It says here that people suffering from extreme mental disorders are unlikely to think virtuously enough to be able to aid themselves - they need other people to help them.'

Aristocles became silent - he seemed lost for words or unwilling to respond; then he asked: 'I assume you are familiar with Plato's story about the cave?'

I nodded in reply and sipped my cappuccino as I waited for Aristocles to continue with his thought-line. 'The story is about prisoners who are forced to face one way so that they can only see shadows of puppets on the cave wall. They think the shadows are real because that's all they see, but there are some prisoners who are not convinced and so they break free and escape. The route out is not easy and at the cave entrance they become blinded by the force of the sun. Some turn back in the belief that the shadows they left behind must be the real world, but the ones who persevere grow accustomed to the light and become enlightened by the true nature of things.'

Aristocles stared into my eyes and said: 'What do you think the story is trying to tell us?'

'I would say the story is used metaphorically to show the difference between those who seek for knowledge and those who don't. The difference being that one path leads to wisdom and the other path to ignorance.'

'That is one interpretation but there is another interpretation,' he replied. 'The story is also about compassion and kindness. Those who escape the cave come back and help others to unshackle themselves. We must do good to strangers and friends, and that includes those who have mental problems and find it difficult to look after themselves.'

'I agree. But the implication of the story is that you can't help others unless you unshackle yourself first.'

'You're right! But we can't just think about ourselves without giving thought to the wellbeing of others?'

'But you've already implied that some people are beyond help. Plato writes that people are imprisoned in their bodies like oyster shells and enlightenment is only available for the few. It's only available for those who make the effort to metaphorically leave the cave and do something with their lives!'

'Yes, I know the argument well, but life is not always clear cut!' Aristocles replied, quite forcibly. 'Plato also informs us that we see through a glass dimly, but that can never be an excuse to stop us from trying to see what is real. After all, even the prisoners, looking at the shadows on the cave wall, can have insights and so it is up to the more enlightened amongst us to help those who are less so. In terms of our discussion, we're back to the concept of the good again.'

'In what way?' I asked.

'Throughout the ages, people have helped others through the kindness of their hearts. They've abandoned what they're doing to help others despite the consequences and often they do so regardless of their own mortal welfare. When people do this, they are responding to a call of goodness within them. You had that call, Alecta, when you dropped everything to look after your mother. You also helped and then befriended Lisa – a young, homeless girl who had been thrown on to the streets by the actions of her rich father!'

I felt tears welling up again. ' ... I couldn't have done any of this without help from my friends and my brother's love.'

'I know more than you realise I know,' he replied mysteriously. 'You were there when they needed you. Goodness is something you do even though the experience can make you feel empty inside. There is no guarantee it will make you happy but there's every chance you will come through as a better person.'

'So happiness is something we cannot aim for when we respond to a call of goodness?' I asked, dabbing my cheeks dry, but feeling thrilled about what Aristocles had just said.

'That's correct - although Plato would say that the soul can hope for happiness.'

'So, would you say, in conclusion, from what we've said so far, that a person can achieve mental wellbeing without being happy?'

'That would seem to be the logical conclusion. It is acts of goodness that bring about mental wellbeing - not happiness. There is a paradox with happiness – if you make it your aim in life to find it, you never will!'

'All this would be revolutionary if it was to take hold of modern-day consciousness!' I exclaimed. 'Self-help books relating happiness to mental wellbeing is a billion dollar business. Writers make a lot of money by relying on simple 'tick-a-box' answers to not-so-simple personal problems in an attempt to convince respondents they can increase their happiness if the right boxes are ticked! ... There are also books that have made millions of dollars for the authors by convincing readers they can achieve happiness by getting themselves attuned to a universal law of attraction that guarantees to future-proof their financial wishes!'

'We'll have to come up with a new category of sophists at this rate!' he replied. 'But seriously, there are never any straight forward answers except for the search for the good in life. Those who seek enlightenment are the ones who are prepared to become better people. Mental wellbeing is only achievable when someone finds the good in their own life by helping other people.'

'There is a Buddhist aspect to all this,' I suggested. 'If we are to do good acts that enhance our mental welfare then we must become less selfish.'

'That is true - I've read about Buddhism in my village; however, unlike Buddhism, Plato's philosophy has goodness, not happiness, as the ideal. But I agree with you, there are many aspects that are similar. Both philosophies stress that we need to dismantle our egos if we are going to make any moral headway.'

'The problem though is trying to do something with those people who delude themselves into thinking they are more virtuous than they really are!'

'I sense you have in mind all those sophists again!' Aristocles exclaimed.

'Writing a thesis about them can make you obsessed!' I replied flippantly. 'I've been thinking - is it possible for sophists to carry out good deeds?'

Aristocles gazed hard at me with his blue eyes and had a sip of his coffee. 'They are capable of good deeds in a publicly acceptable sense,' he answered. 'Any of us can help an old lady across the street. The problem is - they can use their surplus wealth to contribute to charitable causes with the intention that such deeds may bring about career advancement, public recognition and honours. As a consequence, they are unlikely to achieve any lasting wellbeing in their lives because they are so ego-driven.'

'I thought it was only me who had a cynical side!' I replied.

'Sophists will always be sophists,' he replied, scratching of his beard as if trying to get rid of them. 'They are synonymous with the prisoners shackled in Plato's cave. The only hope for them is to unshackle their egos and make their way out of the cave. That's the only way they can know what goodness really means.'

'So, from what you've said, is the implication that no-one can experience goodness?' I asked.

'Goodness can never be experienced. Goodness is something that transcends experience. It is something beyond us that reaches out to us. We become aware of other people's suffering and are driven to help them regardless of any loss to ourselves.'

'It seems that the search for the good in life is mysterious and elusive.'

'It can feel that way. We suffer but we come through it all as better people. Morality is related to our inward journey and is nothing to do with doing acts that demand public recognition.'

' ... and, I assume, a sense of wellbeing also grows within us as we go on our life's journey.'

'That is so ... I think we can conclude from our discussion that happiness is fleeting and unpredictable whereas spiritual wellbeing is something that blossoms within us.'

'We are the metaphorical rose buds ready to open our petals to the world,' I replied.

'I never thought about it in those terms,' he chuckled, making me laugh as well.

We both relaxed and began to chat about other things. Inevitably, as we sipped our cappuccinos dry, the talk drifted back to our beloved Greece. Aristocles wanted to be reminded of the blue Mediterranean Sea along the rocky shores and the fishing boats in the port of Piraeus. His recollection was strange as he talked about sea battles with the Persians and other peculiar events that I couldn't associate with - but I let him talk on. Our reverie continued until a sudden gust of wind hit the café window. We turned our heads and gazed out at the late afternoon sky, darkening with rain.

'I had better make tracks!' I said, with a deep sigh. 'Once again, thanks so much for your help and also your company - you've cheered me up a great deal.'

'It's my pleasure!' Aristocles replied, holding his hand

to his breast. 'Do you think you will be able to complete your thesis now?'

'You've given me lots of inspiration for me to finish fairly quickly now and, hopefully, I'll be back home for Christmas.'

'What will you do with yourself once you're back in Greece?'

'I shall help Yanis run the farm but I'm hoping to start my own academy. There are plenty of out-buildings that can be converted into living quarters and teaching rooms.'

'What would you teach?'

'I will teach about health and wellbeing along with eating and drinking as nature intended us to. There will be enough natural produce on the farm to sustain everyone.'

'What a wonderful idea!'

'I need to believe I can do something to make a difference, even if it's in a small way!'

'Plato was all for pursuing our dreams especially when they have virtuous intent. He would want us to do something extraordinary in our lives and not lie on our backs and do nothing. You need to pass on your passion and wisdom to the students in your care.'

'Hopefully, I can.'

'Let goodness be your guide. It would seem that you will be opening a new academy to rival Plato's original one!'

'I don't know about that but, hopefully, it would have similar features and, I even envisage, there might even be a political aspect to it.'

Aristocles screws up his eyes and asked: 'In what way

do you mean?'

'The students must be aware of the deviousness of all those sophists we've identified!'

Aristocles smiled and said: 'I can see it's going to be a well-balanced curriculum ... I wish you well!'

I smiled and started to put my notes and books into her bag. 'You had better put this one in,' Aristocles said, pointing to the book he had borrowed. 'I won't need it again. I've read all I want and I can now report back to my friends once I return.'

'What will you report on?' I asked, as I started to put my coat on.

'I've been asked to report on the reasons why fewer people are coming to our world after they have departed this one. I have now collected sufficient information to report back and it's unlikely we'll meet again in this way.'

My mouth opened wide as I sat back down with my coat half-buttoned. Aristocles smiled at my bemused expression. 'I've enjoyed our meetings – the coffees but especially being with you,' he remarked.

I glared at him and said: 'I think you have been playing some kind of game with me ... who are you, really?'

'I suppose now is the time to tell you who I really am. My real name is Aristocles but people knew me best as Plato, which is the nickname my students gave me when I was teaching in the Academy in Athens. When I sent you that first communication, I couldn't just say I was Plato. You never would have come! So I decided to use my real name - Aristocles.'

'You can't be Plato - he died over 2,000 years ago!' I exclaimed. 'How do you expect me to believe you're him? Are you some kind of eccentric thespian acting out your role as Plato? ... or some kind of ghost?'

'Look at me, do I look like a ghost?' he protested, with his hands outstretched. 'What I have to tell you will be difficult for you to comprehend but I need you to know. I come from a parallel universe close to this one. When I died all those years ago, I slipped into this other world. I have been resident there ever since, along with other people I know such as Socrates, Aristotle and other interesting people ... We have great debates, I can tell you!'

'I don't believe you. It's far too fanciful!' I retorted. 'No matter who you are, you still haven't been totally honest with me. What is your real reason for meeting up with me?'

'Bafflement!' he replied mysteriously, with his eyes suddenly fixed upon me. 'As I've already said, we have great debates but we are increasingly baffled as to why fewer people are entering our world. We have this tentative belief that more and more humans are entering the outer spheres. If this is true, we can only assume it is because their minds have not developed sufficiently to allow them to make it through to the world we now reside in.'

'It sounds too much like science fiction to me!' I interjected.

'I *am* Plato ... I'm telling you the truth! ... But, if you prefer, I'm just an elderly scholar who wishes to guide you in your own research and, at the same time, gain knowledge of this modern world that I know so little about.'

' ... And where does my Grandfather fit into all this? Did you really know him or is it another bit of your subterfuge?'

'I know your Grandfather very well and we have a special bond between us … Believe me or not, Michal is back in my village waiting for my return, and eagerly waiting for news about you!'

I gave out a big sigh and sat staring at him. I just couldn't take it all in. Who was this person really and what was he hoping to gain by continuing with this deception? After awhile, I said: 'I don't know what to say but, let's assume I go along with this story of yours - just for the time being. What I'd like to know is how did you get here if, as you say, you come from another world?'

'That's easy to answer although the method is technically hard to describe,' he replied, holding his rainbow stick up high. 'This is more than an aid to steady the gait of an old man, it has the ability to transport me into different worlds … all I need to know is where the Teleo-portals are located.'

'What are Teleo-portals?' I asked, becoming more and more suspicious.

'The nearest one is the Queen Victoria's statue where we meet up,' he replied. 'If I didn't have my rainbow stick with me, I would be stranded in your world. That's why I always asked you to look after it every time I went to the counter to get our cappuccinos.'

I became silent trying to comprehend everything. There was too much for me to take in. Could this person just be a kind, old cranky academic who has come into my life to help me with my studies, who happens to have known my Grandpa? … Or is there more to his story? 'I don't know what to say,' I exclaimed, after awhile. 'None of it makes sense but, no matter who you are and where you've come from, I'm sad when you say we'll never meet again. You've not only helped me with my work but also

I've come to regard you as a friend who has steered me through worrying times, and who has believed in me ... Are you sure we'll never meet again?'

'Perhaps not in this lifetime,' he replied solemnly.

I stretched out my arms and together we held hands. There were tears of sadness and joy as we gazed silently at one another. Eventually, I pulled away, and finished putting on my coat. 'Will you walk me to the statue like we always do?'

Aristocles nodded in reply and together we walked out into the darkness. We crossed the tramlines – now, shining snakes of steel against the city lights. We walked across the square until we reached the statue, hardly visible in the growing darkness.

'Well, goodbye,' said Aristocles. 'Avtio.'

'Avtio,' I replied sadly.

'Promise me one thing ... Above all, do something extraordinary in your life.'

'I promise,' I replied automatically.

We searched for one another's eyes. 'I've got something for you?' he said, and thrust one of his hands into his breast pocket.

I looked down at what he had placed in my hand. I could make out a round object. I turned it over and saw it was a brooch. Not just any brooch, but the one that was given to my mother by my father on their wedding day.

'How did you .... !' I cried, as tears streamed down my face. I looked down at the familiar object, turning it round and round in my hand. There was a flash of light. As I raised my head, I knew that Aristocles was no longer there. I walked to the other side of the statue but he was gone!

'Who is this person?' I pondered, as I stared into the blackness of the stone.

In the weeks to come, this same question would come back to me as I sat in the library or walked alone around Whitworth Park ... But I couldn't tell the others - it was my secret ... Aristocles was part of my life and I wasn't prepared to share him with anyone.'

Ever since our first meeting in May, seeming long ago now, I thought there was something of the wizard about him. The way he turned up in my life, grey of hair and beard with a rainbow stick for a wand, and yet, he had an air of a distinguished philosophy professor about him. But, as I imagined him in my thoughts, I couldn't accept that he was actually Plato. The whole thing was too bizarre, even though his final disappearing trick was spectacularly convincing. It was all beyond my comprehension and belief.

As the weeks passed by, his smiling face would often come to me and, in my mind, I would smile back. A great calm would descend and my hand would reach out to touch something I couldn't comprehend - my mother's brooch clipped lovingly on my breast.

Ogres and Gods

I finished my thesis a month after I last saw Aristocles and presented it to Doctor Pendlebury with some trepidation. When we met up in his office a week later, I was expecting his customary lukewarm response but, to my surprise, he was delighted and said it was one of the best Master's theses he had ever read and was particularly impressed how I was able to relate Plato's philosophy to understanding mental health problems in today's society. He asked me if I wanted to carry on my studies at a doctoral level to which I replied it would have to be on a part-time basis as I planned to return to Greece within the month. He was very understanding and wished me all the best for the future, with the promise that we must keep in touch. I came away thinking that Doctor Pendlebury was one of life's unsung heroes who had no intention of joining the ranks of the egotists and self-servers.

There were things to do before I could return to Greece – books to return to the library, tidying up my university desk and flat, and making up parcels of bric-a-brac and books to be sent home ahead of me. By mid-December, I had finished most tasks so there was time to socialise with fellow students and, of course, with Lisa. During the day, we would go round Manchester together – the galleries, the museums and the Arndale Shopping Centre where I bought her extra clothes and shoes.

Most days, we would meet up for lunch at the Whitworth Gallery with Christiana and Morris. We chatted about lots of things but Lisa's mother was always foremost in our minds. Morris had not received any communication from the house in Wilmslow and was seriously thinking about paying them another visit using his guise as a plain clothes policeman. Lisa wasn't too keen on the idea, and then Morris suggested they both go together and confront them head on. 'Just leave it!' she replied, shaking her head.

Christiana was still upbeat about finding Lesley (as she now called Lisa's mum) and was following up several leads from her website. We were amazed at the amount of time she had spent trying to find her. She had systematically searched through all the missing persons' sites in the country and had even gone to Chester and asked lots of homeless people whether they knew of a middle-aged woman sleeping rough. Morris thought what she had done was commendable but said it was like looking for a needle in a haystack. He then announced he had a practical solution to one of Lisa's problems but, despite our questioning, wouldn't elaborate on what it could be.

One week before Christmas, we were seated in the restaurant waiting for Morris to join us. When he finally arrived, he declared, almost formally, he had something important to tell us. He had arranged for a charity to provide bed and breakfast for Lisa in one of their hostel for a minimum period of six months, which meant she would now have a permanent address from which she could apply for jobs. Lisa screamed with joy and flung her arms around him. We all gathered round and hugged him, which he seemed to enjoy; but, in his usual straight-faced way, he said it was nothing really. We all knew he had put a lot of effort into procuring a place for Lisa even though, we suspected, he had used his father's influence in doing so.

Morris also informed us that the place wasn't available until early January and so Lisa would have to spend a second Christmas on the streets - or so it seemed. But, when we met up again, two days later, Christiana declared that Lisa was going to stay with her for Christmas. It was good news but I felt a little peeved because I was planning to ask her myself. When I phoned Yanis the following day, I told a white lie by saying I had to stay in Manchester to look after Lisa. I was surprised that he didn't express any disappointment; in fact, he remarked it was an excellent idea and not to worry about coming home until the New Year.

Over the Christmas period, we spent a lot of time in the bars around the university and we took Lisa to the Christmas Market in Albert Square. Morris had to go back to Oxfordshire to see his parents but he was back after three days saying he'd missed everyone. We continued to have fun but there was a growing sense of things coming to an end.

I booked a flight to Athens once the New Year celebrations were over, but they wouldn't let me go without a farewell party. It took place in Christiana's house on the night before I was due to leave. I arrived to find her parents were there from the Netherlands; they were on a mission to visit the great cathedrals of Canterbury, Glastonbury and Wells. Christiana's father had planned to do a series of paintings from pencil sketches and photographs. They announced they were taking Christiana and Lisa with them in their mobile home to give them both a well-deserved holiday.

The evening itself was a mixture of happiness and sadness as we knew this particular chapter in our lives was about to close. The drink heightened our emotions but it failed to make us cheerful. Christiana's mum got a karaoke going using a portable microphone – we joined in, but our hearts weren't really in it.

I came home to Greece and the family farm near Marathon on the same day I had flown to Manchester, a year earlier. It was mild although the top of Mount Pentelikon was white with snow. I was pleased to be back.

In those first few weeks, I did the round of catching up with friends and family, I went to Athens to visit Nadir and my other university friends - frequenting the usual bars and sharing stories of our collective past. In the mornings, I would go to my favourite café on Solonos street and sip my cappuccino in the winter sunshine. I thought about Aristocles whilst I was there - I missed him.

When I returned to the farm, a young woman was there. Yanis introduced me to Anna and, immediately, I thought: 'So you're the reason why my brother wasn't keen about me coming home for Christmas!' But I was pleased; she seemed good for him and, as we chatted, I had a premonition they would get married and she would come and live on the farm.

The first month soon passed by. I spent the time tidying up the house and sorting out my mother's possessions; there were three piles – for recycling, to keep, and gifts for family and friends. There was an Aztec bracelet of hers which I had always liked so I kept that for myself.

I hadn't heard anything from the early birders until I received an email from Morris at the end of January. It said that Lisa was settled in at the hostel and was now working part time in a store nearby. I emailed back saying I was delighted and how I missed everyone. Christiana emailed me shortly afterwards informing me that her parents were now back in the Netherlands but thought it was a disgrace that her father was questioned for a whole hour at Ijmuiden because of his criminal record. She also said she was planning to come out and see me in the summer - hopefully with Morris and Lisa. I emailed back saying they were always welcome.

The sixth of February would have been Grandpa's birthday. The day was cold but sunny and so Yanis and I planned to go for a trek to the foothills of Mount Pentelikon like we used to do when we were young; he asked if Anna could come too. As we walked, they told me something I'd guessed already – they were getting married in the summer and would I have any objections to Anna living at the farm. I kissed them both and said I was pleased for both of them. I then told them about my plans to start an academy using the outbuildings as classrooms and living quarters – I made it clear I had not thought it all through but, hopefully, I could get some kind of government grant. They thought it was a good idea and said they would help to make it a success.

As we approached the mountain, we saw two birds high up, circling. 'Lammergeyers!' we both shouted and were transported back to our childhood. They circled high above our heads as if they were giving us a blessing. I thought they were Mama and Grandpa who had come back to tell us all was well and to grieve no more. Since I was a child, I believed there were spirits that could break through from other worlds - harbingers from the gods or the gods themselves. No wonder the ancients were envious of birds that could soar so high!

We came back from our trek tired but in high spirits; the coffee tasted good as we talked about the wedding arrangements in the kitchen. I knew I would get on well with Anna; I sensed she had deep well of love within her. As we chatted on, she wanted to know about Grandpa, and so we reminisced about our childhood. We told her he always seemed to be in a happy mood but he could be mischievous when he wanted to be. Yanis told the story of when he was bullied at school. The following afternoon, Grandpa was waiting in the playground with a big bar of chocolate in his hand. He called the bully over, whispered something in his ear, and gave him the chocolate bar. From then on, the boy left Yanis alone. We thought that Grandpa must have been using some kind of reverse psychology or, maybe, as Anna suggested, he was a 'bully-whisperer' - we all laughed at that!

Anna and Yanis had arranged to cook the dinner so I left them to it and retired to Grandpa's study. It was strange sitting in his chair and gazing through the side window to the outside garden where the goats were happily chomping on the oregano through the fence. I opened my laptop and checked my emails - there was one from Morris. I read the first line - 'Hi Alecta, Good news. We have found Lisa's mum!'

Tears of joy flowed down my cheeks as I skimmed through the text. It read that Christiana had sent a letter to the house in Wilmslow giving details about the website she had set up. Maureen must have had a pang of guilt as, shortly afterwards, Morris received an email from her admitting that Lisa's mother and her friend had been back to the house asking for news about Lisa, and there was a Chester telephone number included. On phoning, it soon became clear that Lesley had been staying with her friend for over a year.

It also gave an account of the day Lesley went missing

- how she found an unsealed letter addressed to her husband; it was from Maureen and the contents revealed how they were planning to hive off the family money and buy a holiday home in Spain. I then read how she had fainted and hit her head whilst travelling to her friend's house and ended up in a Manchester hospital with chronic amnesia. For three months, the police could not trace who she was as nobody had reported her missing.

I rushed through to the kitchen and shouted that Lesley had been found! Yanis and Anna came over and gave me a hug, and wanted to know everything there was to tell, but I couldn't tell them as my mind was all over the place, so I dashed back to the study and re-read the whole thing.

Lisa and her mum were the only topic of conversation over dinner. There were bits that seemed incredible to us. Why did she have to go and hit her head and lose her memory on that particular day making it impossible for her to phone Lisa later on? We concluded she must have been under a tremendous amount of stress. Her friend from Chester called Kate came up a lot in the conversation – apparently, she was a solicitor.

On that fateful day, Lisa's mum must have decided to stay with her to ask her advice. Kate wondered what had happened when she didn't turn up so she phoned her home that evening and many times afterwards but nobody ever answered - the phone must have been disconnected or the number changed. She contacted the Cheshire police who didn't seem to be that interested and then, months later, after reading in the newspaper about a woman losing her memory, she travelled to Manchester where she was able to identify Lesley from the police photographic records; by which time Lisa had been living on the streets for several months.

What cheered us up the most was the bit in the email where it read that Kate had written a letter to Lisa's father stating that divorce proceedings were now underway, and the house will have to be sold and half the estate must go to Lesley. Yanis clasped his wine glass and exclaimed: 'Justice has been done! Here's to Lisa and her mum!' We raised our glasses and clinked them resoundingly together. 'To Lisa and her mum!' we cried.

Anna insisted they would do the dishes so I went back into Grandpa's study with my glass of wine and switched on the lamp. I sat there at his desk happily looking around at dusty old books, and the paintings of ancient philosophers gazing back at me from shadowy walls. I had a strong sense of his presence; after all, it was his birthday and his pipe was resting in the ashtray as if he had just gone out. There was a compulsion within me to look at the old black and white photos so I went over to the shelf and came back with one of the albums. There were lots of Grandpa and Grandma taken around the farm and there were a few on a beach I couldn't recognise. Many of them were snapped from low down and there were some with the tops of heads missing. I soon realised who had taken them – my mother as a child. I turned the pages and there were plenty more, some of Mama as a child digging on a beach and one of her wriggling on Grandma's knee.

I was half way through when I came across a photo of two men sitting outside a café in the sunshine – not just any café but *my* café on Solonos Street. When I looked closer I could see that one was Grandpa, and the other was Aristocles. My heart skipped a beat - I couldn't believe it! What was peculiar was that Grandpa looked in his early forties but Aristocles was an old man – the same old man I had met in Manchester! I picked up a magnifying glass and examined him in more detail. His hair and beard were white, his suit was the same, and at his side was his rainbow stick. I couldn't believe it but there he was before my eyes! As I looked closer, I saw there was a child-shaped shadow on the pavement before them and, in between the two coffees on the table, was a bottle of lemonade and a glass. Mama must have taken the photo when she was a girl.

There was too much to take in. I guessed the photo was taken after the war in the late forties or early fifties. It was definitely Aristocles, but why was he just as old then as he was when I met him last year? There he was, smiling for the camera, in my favourite café with Grandpa and Mama; he knew them both but neither of them had said anything about him during their lifetimes. It was a complete mystery. And then, I began to wonder again who Aristocles really was - or is! He didn't lie to me after all – he knew Grandpa as a friend and maybe, all the rest was true. Perhaps, he really is Plato who comes back every now and then to investigate what is happening in this crazy world of ours.

In the half light of the study I pondered all this and more besides. It was still a mystery to me. Thinking back, when I met Aristocles for the first time, he seemed to know so much about me - the fact that he knew both Grandpa and Mama (and possible me as a small child) made everything more likely. So maybe, he sought me out in Manchester not just to keep an eye on me as a promise to my Grandfather but because he knew my mother was dying and was there to comfort me in any way he could. I remember what he said to me about responding to a call of goodness when I decided to fly back home to care for her. Then, I thought again about the possibility of him actually being Plato. It didn't seem likely, but there he was in that photo looking the same as I last saw him last November, with his rainbow stick by his side.

As I sipped my wine, I thought - why shouldn't he be Plato? An enlightened soul destined to come back to shed philosophical light on a world full of sophistry and greed? As human beings, we think we know all the answers, but there will always remain something we cannot rationalise about. Why shouldn't there be other worlds that entities can slide through into ours? Portals that allow spiritual avatars, and even the gods themselves, to come in to our world for reasons known only to themselves, and then go back with their quests complete. Aristocles must have been one of these spiritual beings.

I gazed at Grandpa's five volumes of Plato's dialogues before me and ran my finger along them as I did as a child. I took another sip of wine and selected one of the volumes at random; it fell apart at one of the pages. I read:

'To tell of other divinities, and to know their origin is beyond us, and we must accept the traditions of the men of old time who affirm themselves to be the offspring of gods'.

I felt as though I was back in the café on Market Street with Aristocles. I could hear his voice clearly saying: 'Goodness is what we must strive for in life despite all that life throws at us.'

My mind then drifted and I thought about Lisa, and then Morris and Christiana, and Yanis and Anna. I thought about Kate, Doctor Theo and Doctor Pendlebury - all of them doing things to help others, out of the goodness of their hearts without wanting any recognition or reward. And then, I thought about all the sophists in the world – Lisa's father, the capitalists, the perpetrators of fake news, the tricksters and pedlars of dubious goods, the exploiters of people's lives, and those who stopped John Yudkin from doing good research for the sake of their own exalted esteems. These are the ogres of greed spewing out their vomit into the world - turning truth to lies, polluting our food, poisoning our lands, and being in perpetual denial of their involvement in creating huge islands of plastic bags and throwaway bottles in our oceans.

I picked up the magnifying glass and looked again at Aristocles in the photo. He seemed to be smiling back at me and saying: 'Do something extraordinary in your life to make it a better world.' I smiled back and said 'I will!'

I replaced the album on the shelf and returned to the kitchen with an empty wine glass in my hand. I could smell the wonderful aroma of coffee.

Plato's World

This is Chapter 1 of my thesis (including notes and references) as presented to Doctor Pendlebury in February of the year I was at the University of Manchester – Alecta.

The aim of this review is to examine Plato's anatomical and practical ideas on health within the wider context of Greek society during the fourth and third centuries BC. The customs, practices and belief systems prevalent at this time shaped Plato's thoughts and writings on health but, from our 21st century perspective, how can we make sense of things that happened so long ago? If we gaze down the lens of an imaginary time camera, it should enable us to perceive a range of snapshots of what life was like and trust in our own imagination to gain an insight into the minds of the ancient Greeks. There is no doubt that we have much in common with our ancestors by the very nature of our human condition but our modern society has shaped our minds in a distinctive way. The ancient Greeks were unique and idiosyncratic in their own way too; they had a fierce joy of living and an acute awareness of the shortness and unpredictability of life. They were fatalistic and alert to their own hubristic behaviour that could anger the gods to mete out storms, war, pestilence and all manner of human afflictions. They were also capable of great debate and had a strong appreciation of poetry and drama penned by writers such as Homer, Hesiod and Sophocles.

Social Order and War

One of the first things to get into perspective in ancient Greece is the smallness of the city-state where the people lived with their families and neighbours. Today, we are used to living in countries with populations of tens or even hundreds of millions but, in Plato's world, it would be inconceivable to think of governments being responsible for more than 20,000 citizens. The city-state or polis meant more to the Greeks than just a seat of government, it represented the whole communal life of people including their cultural, moral and economic welfare. There would have been several hundred city-states within Greece and its colonies of southern Italy and Sicily; the most important and largest was Athens where Plato was born and lived for most of his life. The fourth century BC saw the rise of Athens as a political power whose influence was based on democracy rather than the rule of kings.

The medium for democratic debate was the Assembly where decisions were made on the running and survival of the city-state. During the fourth century BC, Athens was arguably the most civilised society ever to have existed and this reached its apotheosis under Pericles who was appointed leader of the Assembly, almost undisputed, from 461 BC until his death in 429 BC. Under his stewardship, Athens went through a period of peace with its arch-enemies

Sparta and Persia. During this era there was a great surge in artistic and architectural achievements including the construction of the Parthenon, the temple erected in honour of Athena, Athens' patron deity. It was also a period of theatre-going and intellectual debate much of which took place in the open air where the people could take advantage of the warm Mediterranean climate.

Under Pericles' leadership, Athens became powerful and influential. Over 100 cities joined a voluntary confederacy and Athens' political influence and wealth flourished but, after several decades of peace, the various treatises fell apart and war with Sparta erupted in 431 BC throughout most of the Greek world. The war raged almost continually until 404 BC, during this time much of the hinterland around Athens was destroyed by the Spartan army and the country-dwellers were forced to abandon their homes and take refuge within the walls of Athens. The cramped unsanitary conditions caused a plague which killed a third of the population including Pericles himself. The devastation caused by war and plague led to a tragic decline of the Athenian spirit and the subsequent devaluation of the polis as a vehicle for democratic debate and action. Eventually, with the collusion of Sparta, an oligarchy took power - a group of revengeful politicians known as 'The Thirty'. The people of Athens were subject to a rule of terror and political chaos for several months before there was a restoration of the Assembly; the outcome, however, was not as the people were used to - democracy had returned in a weakened and restricted form.

The war with Sparta had a profound effect on the Athenians of every social class. Plato was 23 years old when the hostilities finally ended; his philosophical writings over the next 50 years were greatly influenced by the war and the decline of the polis since the untroubled early years of Pericles. The catalyst, which arguably had the greatest influence on Plato's philosophical ideas, was the death of his tutor, Socrates, who was sentenced to end his life by the restored Athenian Assembly on trumped-up charges of corrupting the young and refusing to honour the official gods of the state. In Plato's Apology[1], Socrates' defence of these accusations is portrayed in dialogue between himself and his accusers. He denies all the crimes laid against him by stating that he is incapable of corrupting the city's youth as he possesses no wisdom whatsoever and does not believe in the gods anyway. His ardent defence fell on deaf ears possibly because Socrates made his prominent Athenian accusers look foolish in public but, just as likely, because he had been past friends with Alcibiades and Critias who were both indicted for their involvement with 'The Thirty' oligarchy.

Socrates became the central character in Plato's philosophical writing. In most of the dialogues, he is the main character who is there to question others about essential terms such as justice, friendship and courage, and to move people closer to understanding the true meaning of such terms. Within his earlier dialogues[2], we are closest to Socrates' own thoughts and ideas. In his later writings, he used the character of Socrates to disseminate a philosophy that goes beyond Socrates' own beliefs. In the Republic, Plato put forward his own exposition of the ideal state in which citizens should be educated to use their talents for the benefit of the whole society[3]. The hierarchical political system described in the Republic was conceived by Plato after witnessing the shameful treatment of Socrates by the so-called democratic assembly and, as a consequence, became disillusioned with democracy as a force for good. He proposed a society where the people would be ruled by an elite class known as the guardians. They would be trained with the task of ruling; the rest of society would be made up of soldiers and citizens having specialised skills in crafts and trade. The greatest happiness of the whole would be achieved by everyone pulling together for the greater good. There would be a class distinction of sorts as every citizen would know their place in the order of things and even the citizens who were selected to become guardians would have to contribute significantly to the common good of everyone in the city-state.

Plato's ambition to provide a philosophical blueprint for an ideal society may have been formulated through good intentions, but from a present day perspective the basic design is somewhat flawed. Plato's notion of an ideal state, for example, did not apply to slaves as they were not regarded as freemen of the city. They could try to buy their freedom through the Athenian courts, but those that remained slaves had no place in Plato's philosophy. They had no responsibilities or privileges as citizens of the city including having no right to attend and vote in the Assembly. Plato's utopian vision for a better world in the fourth and third centuries BC was based on his own insights and knowledge of the world he was born into and the benefits derived from having a good education and a comfortable upbringing. He did not want to do away with the social structure that he was familiar with and found no inconsistency in having an underclass of slaves working for the legitimate citizens. What he wanted was for the people of Athens to function more harmoniously for the greater good and happiness of the people.

He strove for a more just and stable society where citizens would know their place but could be given the opportunity to 'rise through the ranks' if they proved themselves worthy. This applied technically to both genders as revealed in the Republic[4]; Plato envisaged the possibility of women becoming guardians but only if they were of the right calibre and capable of practicing bare-chested along with the men at military training. However, this peculiar vision of Plato's contradict what was actually happening in Athens at that time; women were mostly considered to be inferior to men with the expected role of managing the household and, more importantly, to bear and raise legitimate children.

Medical Beliefs and Practices

Many of these social divisions and practices would be considered abhorrent if encountered in our modern world but for Plato, as envisaged in his Republic, they would be essential for creating a fairer and more cohesive social order. Many of his philosophical ideas were already embedded within early Greek society and he saw no reason to change the status quo if he thought that the city-state would benefit from the continuation of various established practices. This can be seen in the way he distinguishes between the practices of two classes of doctors in Athens – one for the freemen (and supposedly their families) and one for their slaves[5]. He refers to the former as the gentler kind of physician compared with the ruder type of the latter:

" ... the slave doctors run about and cure the slaves, ... practitioners of this sort never talk to their patients individually, or let them talk about their own individual complaints ... But the other doctor, who is a freeman, attends and practises upon freemen; and he carries his enquiries far back, and goes into the nature of the disorder; he enters into discourse with the patient and with his friends, and is at once getting information from the sick man, and also instructing him as far as he is able, and he will not prescribe for him until he has first convinced him; at last, when he has brought the patient more and more under his persuasive influences and set him on the road to health, he attempts to effect a cure."

Plato's writings on health relates to this gentler sort of physician who has the time to communicate with his 'freemen' patients as he tries to assess and diagnose their underlying medical condition. He is against the type of doctor who only gives arbitrary commands, although, the assumption is that this approach is good enough for the slaves. The gentler kind of medical practices fits more comfortably with Plato's wider philosophy. In the Phaedrus[6], Socrates explains how any method proceeding without analysis is like the 'groping of a blind man' which implies that the medical practitioner has to use the right application of words when treating a patient. Plato was against the use of speech-making to gain influence over other people with the intention of corrupting their minds[7]; he was particularly against politicians in this respect. However, he believed that rhetoric could be used as a force for good as an art for enchanting the soul[8], which is an essential part of the doctor–patient relationship.

There is evidence in the dialogues to suggest that Plato's portrayal of the gentler sort of physician was influenced by Hippocrates by emphasising aids to recovery that relieve pain by natural means whilst desisting from causing unnecessary harm. Plato would emphasise the importance of the body being understood as a whole and, only after full consultation with the patient, would a regimen have been prescribed based on the physician's knowledge of herbs and other natural remedies[9]. Plato was against extreme medical treatments and practices - crude surgery, nauseating drugs, burnings and starvation were not to be used unless the condition was in an advanced state. He argued that such extreme medical interventions can cause complications to the extent that diseases may multiply through the provoking of a 'disagreeable enemy'[10]. Added to this was the disgrace amongst some physicians of coming up with new conditions to treat which would increase their fees[11].

Plato, along with many of his contemporaries, frowned upon prolonging life unnecessarily[12]; he believed that there are circumstances when the fate of death is more attractive than the continuation of a severely painful existence. In this respect, he criticised a trainer called Herodicus who struggled on to old age with a sickly condition with the aid of his doctors who plied him with medicine and poor advice. In Plato's eyes[13], Herodicus was a valetudinarian - someone who clings on to life at all costs. He believed that Herodicus was the prime mover in bringing about a popular movement in Greece which Plato derogatively named 'the invention of lingering death'.

Broadly speaking, the Hippocratic approach to healing, as portrayed in the dialogues, concentrates mostly upon what we would now term 'the worried-well'. However, physicians in Plato's time were practical people who would do their best to save life regardless of cause. Basic first aid was practiced on the battlefields and medical expertise was adapted for injuries and ailments in the home. However, regardless of context, there was a general acknowledgement that the gods would decree the fate of the diseased or severely injured. Healing and medicine never divorced itself from its religious roots. Prayers and votive offerings would be given to one or more of the healing deities. People were more likely to attribute serious cases of ill-health to hubris and the inability to pay sufficient homage to the appropriate god.

From our 21st century perspective, it would be too easy to look upon the early Greeks' worldview as inferior to our own just because they didn't have to same amount of scientific knowledge as we possess now. We must credit them with some rudimentary scientific knowledge of the world through observing natural phenomena, and they also had a basic appreciation of how the body responded to various medicines. Nevertheless, they did not have an adequate understanding of human anatomy and this limited the doctor's awareness and insight into the causes of the illnesses and maladies of their patients. The physicians were reluctant to perform dissections or autopsies to enhance their knowledge of the internal workings of the human body. This was chiefly because of religious scruples but there was also a singular lack of curiosity and, therefore, erroneous concepts developed as to the functioning of the human physiology. Examples of this can be found in the Timaeus dialogue[14]. Respiration is described as a process in the lungs which somehow enters the belly to liquefy meat and drink before ending up in the veins to assist with the flow of blood around the body. Other peculiar anatomical notions are: hearing is a 'blow' to the ear which ends up in the liver; the spleen acts like a napkin to keep the liver bright and pure; and the purpose of the intestines is to prevent gluttony.

The early Greeks' unwillingness to carry out basic scientific research distorted their views on the causes of human diseases. The plague that devastated the people of Athens including Pericles himself was, in all probability typhus[15], but the common belief at the time was that it was miasma; a pollution brought on by the anger of the gods. More success was had with common human ailments although their lack of anatomical understanding still held them back. Popular opinions at the time would have had a strong influence on the way Plato thought and wrote about diseases of the body; he identified three ways in which they could take hold - by wind, phlegm and by bile[16]. If we look at diseases caused by wind, Plato was aware that the lungs dispensed air to the body and so he concluded that ailments such as bronchitis, coughs and colds were as a consequence of the passageways being restricted by mucous secretions known as rheums. This reasoning was sound enough but, when it comes to more severe cases, it was based on guesswork and supposition rather than sound practical understanding. He thought that an excess of wind forced the air through the veins causing them to swell which could bring about internal decomposition. Diseases relating to phlegm are described as not being too problematical. There is white phlegm which can be dangerous when detained within by air bubbles causing the decay of tender flesh, and there is acid phlegm which is of a catarrhal nature.

The third type of disease associated with bile was thought to be the most serious as it can cause inflammations and tumours. The body loses its capability of regulating the 'fire' within the body thus disturbing the order of the fibres scattered about in the blood. The heat in the body is unable to escape effectively through the skin pores leading to stale blood and a variety of fevers. The worst case scenario is when the fibres in the blood are overcome by heat to the extent that the blood boils. When this burning passes into the marrow this can lead to death; however, when there is less bile in the body, it can be ejected through the veins into the intestines in the form of diarrhoeas and dysenteries.

These medical ideas and practices were very much a part of Plato's ideology as put forward in the Timaeus. Curiously, this was the only one of Plato's text known to the western world until the Middle Ages, translated from Greek into Latin by the Roman politician and philosopher, Cicero. As such, many of Plato's peculiar notions were taken up by future scholars. There was also another influencing factor that impacted upon Plato's ideas in the Timaeus, and that was the belief that the universe was brought into being by a creator god. He conceived god as a divine craftsman with mathematical intelligence bringing about order from disorder. In the beginning, there were elementary particles jostling together in a chaotic manner but eventually formations came about through the combining of particles into mathematical forms. Bizarrely, according to the theory, there were two sorts of right-angled triangles which combined together to form larger triangles and other geometric shapes. Plato was much influenced by Pythagoras, with geometry providing a basis of certainty within a world of chaos; these were thought of as the building blocks of life.

These elementary forms were never in stasis for they were always in conflict in a bid to dominate and to gain ascendancy. The theory goes that they combine together to make up the four broad elements in Plato's physical world of fire, air, earth and water; these 'do battle' with one another in a similar way as the elementary components. The Timaeus informs us that these four elements pervade the human physiology and each of their relative proportions determines the outcome of our bodily health. Although there is continuous conflict between the elements of fire, air, earth and water as they try to penetrate and dominate one another, whenever there is relative harmony, there is a tendency towards good health; whenever there is a persistent imbalance then there is a danger that ill-health and disease will follow. Our bodily functions were conceived by Plato as one of inflows and outflows within a process of repletion and depletion and, when this is disturbed in anyway, there are repercussions for one's health. These healthy or unhealthy balances were seen by Plato as evidence of there being mathematical laws of proportion at play.

The idea of achieving a healthy life by keeping the bodily processes of repletion and depletion in balance is not too far from our own thinking of sustainable health by eating and drinking wisely and exercising on a regular basis. The concept of proportionality can be applied to the metabolic make-up of our bodies and how cell structures can change when disease takes hold. Plato has something to say about the ageing process which has a semblance of concurrence with modern scientific research[17]. Both in the Symposium and the Timaeus, he talks about the perpetual process of loss and reparation, and how bodily components deteriorate as we grow older. He explains that when we are young the finer corporeal elements are strong and easily defeat the elements that invade the body through eating and drinking. However, as we grow older, these internal structures come under more stress through constantly battling with these external elements. Over time, our bodies deteriorate because the external components of food and drink are causing us to waste away more rapidly than the internal processes associated with enhancing life.

This description of bodily decline was conceptualised without the use of microscopes and other modern scientific equipment, and yet, the theory does have similarities with recent research into the ageing process of human cells and their subsequent death. Modern science reveals to us that there is a positive link between the rate of leakage of free radicals within cells and life expectancy. Within our bodies, chemical signals can direct cells to 'take their own life' as a consequence of the leakage rate of free radicals. The faster the free radicals leak, the more rapid and widespread is cell death[18]. Rather than being passive recipients of this chemical process, people can make a decision to restrict the calorie intake of what they eat and drink with the likelihood that they will live longer than people who consume irresponsibly. In other words, with sustained healthy eating and drinking, the cell structures develop more resilient membranes so that leakage of free radicals is much reduced. If we relate this to Plato's terminology, the finer bodily elements are not consumed away as quickly by the external elements associated with the consumption of food and drink.

There is no doubt that there is a chasm between Plato's world of elementary particles and a world brought up to understand the links between DNA, genes and protein molecules. However, there was a conceptualisation amongst ancient Greek scholars like

Plato that led them to believe there were building blocks of matter which constituted the material world. Terms like 'battle' and 'war' were used to suggest conflict from armed aggression or from natural disasters. It is no surprise that these metaphors were also used to describe the inner world of the body as the various elements 'battled' for supremacy causing imbalances of health whenever one sort got the 'upper hand'; or, alternatively, to use another war-associated metaphor, health would be restored during those periods when there was an 'alliance' amongst the competing elements. Although there are curious similarities between modern-day medical science and Plato's pre-scientific model of human physiology, there is still a deficit of understanding. For most Greeks living in the fourth and third centuries BC, truths were more likely to be thought of as being preordained by the gods rather than something that could be discovered by scientific observation and, as a consequence, the way they lived their lives focused on an acceptance of their lot as decreed by forces beyond their control.

So what has our gaze down the lens of our imaginary time camera taught us about Plato's world? They were, as we are, humans with fears, hopes and loves, but their lives were cast into a different historical setting. There were always threats of war, plague and social uncertainty but against this backdrop the citizens of Athens would enjoy literature, plays and philosophical conversations, mostly in the open air by taking full advantage of the Mediterranean climate. Having slaves was the accepted norm who would work whilst their masters enjoyed these finer things in life. There were wide social divisions with wives not having the same rights as their husbands, and doctors practicing different types of medicine according to the status of their patient. Hippocrates and his natural methods of healing are still influential today but, unlike the ancient Greeks, we are more likely to treat people regardless of age and seriousness of the medical condition. The early Greeks held the common belief that the gods decreed when someone's time was up and there was little good in keeping someone alive for the sake of living longer than their natural life span. Plato and his contemporaries tried to explain suffering and disease in their own way according to their own worldview, but their reasoning was too much tied up with explanations unsubstantiated by empirical research. There was an element of guesswork in their deliberations but, nevertheless, they came close to understanding the biological concepts of the ageing process at a time in history that was devoid of microscopes and scientific explanation.

Notes and References – Plato's World:

1. This dialogue is the only one where Plato appears as himself. Overall, it is believed that he wrote 36 dialogues. Throughout this book, I have used my Grandfather's collection of 'The Dialogues of Plato' translated from Greek to English by B. Jowett.

2. The early dialogues of Plato are: Apology, Crito, and Symposium.

3. See Book IV in the Republic for a description of Plato's ideal state.

4. See the Republic 451 to 457 for examples of the type of training for women included military training. This peculiar vision of Plato's seems to contradict what was actually happening in Athens at that time. Women were often considered to be second-class citizens who would have been educated solely on practical skills such as spinning and weaving. This contrasts sharply with the legitimate males who were educated at school to read and write, and were given the opportunity to pursue the finer arts of poetry, music and gymnastics.

5. Laws 720

6. Phaedrus 270

7. Gorgias 452

8. Phaedrus 272

9. See Phaedrus 270 and Charmides 156. The Hippocratic Oath has been greatly influential through the ages for the relieving of suffering and abstaining from causing harm through the use of potent drugs and extreme medical practices. In ancient Greece, however, the oath was part of the initiation into a 'closed shop' of physicians who collected payments from their patients and swore only to divulge their professional knowledge to a selected few.

10. See Timaeus 89, Republic 406, Protagoras 354

11. Republic 405

12. Laches 195

13. Republic 406

14. See Timaeus 73 to 91

15. The most famous epidemic in Greek history was the Athenian plague from 430 to 426 BC causing the death of Pericles and a third of the city's population. The historian, Thucydides, contracted the disease, survived, and then wrote a good account of it by describing people's sufferings and how the symptoms changed as the disease took hold. This was one of the few empirical studies during this period and modern scholars were able to relate Thucydides' findings to modern day understanding of the disease; the most likely candidates are typhus or smallpox.

16. The types of diseases are described in the Timaeus 81 to 86.

17. See Timaeus 81 and Symposium 207.

18. Lane, N. (2009) *Life Ascending.* London: Profile Books. 278 – 281

Notes and References

The following notes and references relate to the conversations I had with Aristocles whilst drinking coffee - most of them went into my thesis – Alecta.

In Search of the Mean:

Page 26:

"I've read about that in his Timaeus; how the four elements of fire, air, earth and water need to be in proportion in order to sustain life" - I have placed a series of footnotes throughout this book as a guide to the references and notes I made whilst writing up my Masters thesis (using Jowett's translation from the Greek). This particular reference relates to Plato's dialogue, the Timaeus. The correct reference is Timaeus 43a, where 43 relates to the page number and the letter 'a' refers to the place on the page (which can range from a to e). In this particular example, the reference indicates the reference is at the beginning (i.e. section 'a' of page 43). This form of referencing was introduced in 1578 by the publisher, Henri Etienne. Hope this helps – Alecta.

Page 27:

"Plato made the distinction between necessary pleasures that enhance health, and those that are unnecessary, usually associated with over-indulgence" - Republic 559a – d

"In the Republic, he wrote about them derogatively as being bloated with waters and winds, and referred to them collectively as - Tyrannical Man" - Republic 405d & Plato 571 to 574. Plato was disparaging towards young Athenian men who he considered to be rich, arrogant and hubristic. He used derogatory terms such as Tyrannical Man, wild beasts and monstrous winged drones to describe their behaviour that was often lustful, drink-fuelled, and out of control.

Page 32:

"Plato's answer to this is that we must seek for a balance between pleasure and pain by living our lives in the mean" - Laws 733c & d. Plato writes we desire to have pleasure, but we neither desire nor choose pain. For a balanced life, we must seek a balance between pleasure and pain, as nature intended.

Page 34:

"Let's assume the concept of soul is the same as the mind, which is what Plato does in several of his dialogues" - In many of Plato's dialogues there is an assumption that there is an afterlife based on an Orphic view that all knowledge is reminiscence and is brought by the soul from a previous existence. However, in some of his dialogues (e.g. the Philebus and Theatetus) the soul is considered to be synonymous with the mind, and can be identified with ordinary consciousness.

"People can get to the stage in their lives where they no longer have the will to think rationally and are not able to help themselves" - Republic 439d

"Plato believed that the body is an endless source of trouble to us and, even when we think we're enjoying ourselves, extreme pleasures can soon bring on pain and disease" - Phaedo 66c

Page 35:

"He wrote that the worst of these diseases occurs when the soul (or, if you prefer – the mind) is driven by uncontrollable passions to the extent that the end result is madness" - Timaeus 86b

Page 36:

"Know Thyself,' I remarked, recalling what I had recently read" - This inscription was written in the forecourt of the Temple of Apollo at Delphi - see Charmides 164d

"In his early writing, he also has Socrates saying 'virtue is knowledge'" Meno 87b – e

Page 37:

He also writes that a variety of experiences can bring about a more pleasurable and healthier life - Laws 797e

"Plato would answer it by saying that no-one goes willingly towards something that is bad for them, although they can be deceived into thinking that their bad habit is doing them good" - Protagoras 358c

Page 38:

"It was, therefore, thought wrong for individuals to hide themselves away for long periods of time as this was thought to be harmful to the whole community" - Common tables had their origins in men having to go to war and the camaraderie that goes with living and fighting together, and it was this military tradition that Plato thought could be applied to city living. See Laws 625f, 626a, 633a, 780c

Page 39:

" ... there will always be people in society who do not, cannot, change the way they behave regardless of how much help they receive, which means they are likely to be faced with some kind of corrective punishment imposed by their community" - Plato was not against punishment by imprisonment if all else fails. Laws 908 – 909

Page 40:

"I remember reading in the Philebus how Plato has Socrates putting forward reasons why the greatest good is attributed to wisdom rather than pleasures of the body" - Plato has Socrates saying that there are pleasures of desire, that are more akin to the body, and there are true pleasures, associated with the mind. As humans we cannot avoid having bodily desires but we must try and avoid the worst kind which he names - the vicious pleasures. These are the ones that drag us away from the mean in the diagram. See Philebus 45d - e

Page 41:

"Socrates writes that a return to the mean is a source of natural pleasure which is where the necessary pleasures reside" - Philebus

31d

Page 42:

"Remember what Plato wrote about the elderly Athenian statesmen?" Plato wrote about three influences that tempted these people to have unhealthy routines, even though the produce was delightful to the palate. Thearion, the baker who made admirable loaves; Mithoccus, who wrote a Sicilian cook book; and Sarambus, the vintner who produced excellent wine. Plato's main message is that these statesmen were more likely to blame their advisors and trainers for giving them bad advice on their regimen rather than blame themselves for over-indulging over so many years. - Gorgias 518b – d

Page 43:

"It's a joke because he says that the children would kill the physician rather than the cook because they would always choose food that was tasty but bad for them rather than the physician's choice of healthy, wholesome food which is not so appealing" - Gorgias 464e

Page 44:

"He talks about the dangers of having too many Syracusan dinners with lots of spices and sweet sauces" - Republic 404d

A Surfeit of Sophists:

Page 59:

"Plato was against programmes of violent exercise as he thought they not only brutalised people but also made them lazy" - see Republic 404a, 411d and Gorgias 456e

"It's in the Republic. It's the nature of the soul that determines what's good for the body and not the other way round" - Republic 403d

Page 66:

"He despised sophists as haters of truth and corrupters of minds" - Sophist 222a – e

Page 70:

" ... being invisible reminds me of a story that Plato recounted in one of his dialogues about a shepherd called Gyges who lived in Lydia" - Republic 359c – e, 360a – b

Page 71:

" ... Socrates would have been there like the proverbial gadfly questioning and testing the veracity of what was being said" - Apology 30e

Page 75:

"Plato would say: it's not being infatuated with our bodies that brings about life benefits but wisdom, and that is the key to a contented life" - See Charmides 173c - d and Euthydemus 280a

Page 78:

"There are lots of examples here of research results being distorted" - For specific examples read: Kendrick. M. (2014) *Doctoring Data: How to sort out medical advice from medical nonsense.* Columbus Publishing Ltd

Page 80:

"In 1972, his book 'Pure, White and Deadly' was published with the main message that sugar is as toxic as smoking and alcohol, and should be consumed sparingly" - Yudkin. J. (1972) *Pure, White and Deadly: How sugar is killing us and what we can do to stop it.* London: Penguin

Page 82:

"They fit well with Plato's description of them - as paid hunters who peddle falsehoods and deceits" - Sophist 223b and 231c

"These types are more likely to go along with mob thinking or, if you like, mob-oratory" - See Nussbaum, M.C. (2010) *Not For Profit: Why Democracy Needs The Humanities.* Princeton: Princeton University Press. p51. and Theatetus 162d

Page 84:

"In Plato's Theatetus, he gives a good explanation of what counts as knowledge and how it differs from mere opinion" - Plato argues in the Theatetus that knowledge is not the same as perception because that which is perceived differs between people and also for the same person over time. At the end of the dialogue, he concludes that knowledge is having a true belief that something is true but a person must put forward a good account as to why that is the case.

Page 85:

"What you've just said seems like you're promoting Plato's noble lie" - Republic 414 and 415 in detail

Goodness and Wellbeing:

Page 97:

"Plato writes that bereavement brings about both pleasure and pain" - Philebus 48a

Page 98:

"Plato writes that the search for knowledge requires us not to be afraid of death. In fact, he says we should desire it!" - Phaedo 64b

Page 99:

"That's fine. Beliefs don't always have to be expressed through words. Actions are also expressions of belief" - Phaedrus 277 – 278

"It says a lot about what Plato identifies as goodness" - Plato discriminates between what is pleasure and what is goodness in the Philebus. See also Timaeus 51d for his discussion of self-existing ideas unperceived by sense and only apprehended by the mind.

Page 100:

"Plato also talks about the joys of experiencing true pleasures that are untainted by pain" - Philebus 51a – c

Page 101:

"His student, Aristotle, continued the debate after Plato, by stating that the soul is divided against itself and is pulled in many directions; and so, we must strive to live our lives in what Aristotle called 'the golden mean' " - Nicomachean Ethics 1166b

Page 102:

"Plato believed that the soul was there before birth and survives after death, but in some of his dialogues he doesn't explicitly make that assumption and writes as if the soul is synonymous with the mind" - As was discussed with Aristocles in the chapter 'In Search of the Mean', there is the assumption in many of Plato's dialogues that there is an afterlife based on an Orphic view that all knowledge is reminiscence from a previous existence. However, in some of his dialogues (e.g. the Philebus and Theatetus) the soul is considered to be synonymous with the mind, and can be identified with ordinary consciousness.

Page 103:

"It says that several modern philosophers regard the concept of mental health as being invented by Plato!" - Read about these writers in: Seeskin, K. (2008) *Plato and the origin of mental health.* International Journal of Law and Psychiatry 31. 487 – 494

"There's a good reference here from the Timaeus,' I said enthusiastically. 'It says that just as the body becomes diseased so does the soul" - Timaeus 86b

"The author also refers to Plato's Philebus by stating that to 'know not thyself' is the opposite to that which is written on the inscription at Delphi - 'know thyself'" - Philebus 48c

Page 104:

"I assume you are familiar with Plato's story about the cave?" - Republic 514 – 516

Page 105:

"We must do good to strangers and friends ... " - Phaedrus 233d – e

"It's only available for those who make the effort to metaphorically leave the cave and do something with their lives!" - Phaedrus 250b –d

Page 106:

"That's correct - although Plato would say that the soul can hope for happiness" - Philebus 32 – 33

Page 110:

"He would want us to do something extraordinary in our lives and not lie on our backs and do nothing" - In Apology 38a, Socrates said, just before his death, that the life which is unexamined in not worth living which implies we must reach out and do something special with our lives.

Ogres and Gods:

Page 125:

"To tell of other divinities, and to know their origin is beyond us, and we must accept the traditions of the men of old time who affirm themselves to be the offspring of gods" - Timaeus 40d

Printed in Great Britain
by Amazon